Creative Writing Workshops London

ANTHOLOGY

A CIP catalogue record for this book is available from the British Library
ISBN-9781838278632

Back cover image and opening face image © 2020 Clemily Martin: contact@clemilymartin.com
Cover logo by Maddie Chandler

Published by Blackbird Digital Books
www.blackbird-books.com

It's all about unleashing the imagination...

Contents

Introduction… p1
FIRST PRIZE Tanda Lula by Elle Spencer… p3
RUNNER-UP The Road to Itacuiaxa by Clemily Martin…. p13
THIRD PRIZE Automatic by Alison Targett... p20
FOURTH PRIZE The Waiting Room by Ricky Cibardo... p24
The Big 5 Oh by Lisa Barrett... p29
Blue Masquerade by T C Bridgeman... p36
Untitled by Colles Breatic... p41
The Rabbit Hole by Angela Buckell... p44
Moonland by Otilia Galca... p51
The Obituary by Vicki Hassett... p59
Perfect Harmony by Glenn Mackenzie… p67
Destiny, A Memoir by Carol Martin-Sperry... p74
Dear Anna by Dia N... p82
Out of the Blue by Karen Pearson... p87
A Cat's Story by Amy Pope... p95
Confessions of a Nun by Violet Spring... p99
Siblings: Notes for a Play by James Thellusson... p107
Circuit by Oksana Wenger... p111
Broken by Gill Williams... p119
1CS Cripple Street by Astrid Wilson... p130
More Information About CWWL... p139

Introduction

The short stories, extracts from novels and memoirs gathered together here are the result of a creative writing competition put together by CWWL, Creative Writing Workshops London, over the summer of 2020.

As we were all adjusting to a very different way of living under lockdown, including the transfer of our writing workshops from a very convivial Chiswick kitchen table with endless tea, coffee, and Diane's home-made chocolate brownies, to Zoom online, we decided to run a not-for-profit writing competition. It was open to all of our alumni writing students. The £5.00 entry fees were put into a pot and divided amongst the 4 winners.

Thank you to Anna Klerfalk of Inter Saga Literary Agency for sharing the (anonymous) judging with us, Amy Assad and Chiswick Buzz TV for the film of the awards party [https://chiswickbuzz.net/blog/awards-for-budding-chiswick-authors], illustrator Clemily Martin, logo designer Maddie Chandler, and to Nick Chandler for giving up his home for the workshops and awards evening.

Most of all, thanks to the writers themselves. We are very proud of the community that is growing around our classes. Our courses are aimed at beginners, and many of the pieces here are by people who have never written a story before in their lives. Others are by those who write as a profession – there are several journalists here, a documentary film director, an advertising copywriter… Whatever their experience of putting pen to paper, it is immensely rewarding for us to be able to share our love for creating stories and then to witness the unleashing of imaginations that happen before our eyes and ears at each and every workshop.

We look forward to many more classes and anthologies to come.

All proceeds from sales of this anthology will go to Chiswick charity The Upper Room.

Diane and Stephanie

The Winner

TANDA LULA

by Elle Spencer

Isiphelo

His body mass swaddled her like the best blankie: safe and snuggly.

The Cape Flats had just rung in 1970. Tanda Lula sucked her thumb as the pain between her legs started again.

The Child was seven. Her rapist, 38.

Inye

There's a Polaroid photo of two parents. It's a pointed plastic weapon. Like a ninja star, only square. After stab, stab, stabbing away at it for some time, it had become lodged in The Child's heart. (It will sit there for decades, as it turns out.)

The parents look disgusting. Monstrously absorbed in each other. Smug in their stupid co-dependency. The kind of couple that sparks hatred in the hammer of a gun held by a jealous loner.

You'd never guess they had a child. While the Polaroid was snapped by the roadside on the edge of Cape Town, The Child had wandered off through the mealy fields.

As was her way on these lonely days.

Even at five, she knew she was peripheral. Hell, her mother had told her so many times that she'd been a 'huge accident'... that there hadn't even been penetration.

It was important a five-year-old knew these things.

They'd stopped to buy a pineapple by the side of the road. The blue backie fluffing up dust as her father braked sharply, announcing his arrival at the layby like the Supreme White Man he thought he was. Wearing a bear-brown cowboy hat, and a go-me grin, he looked like he'd missed the memo that this was South Africa not the Deep South.

Each perfect prickly pineapple cost just 10 cents. They were bought with a flourish, but The Child had no memory of ever tasting their juiciness once they got home.

A wet, cool nose on The Child's hand. One of their German Shepherds, and an unpaid nanny. The Child smiled down at the dog, then looked back towards the road. Perhaps she wouldn't run away, today. She'd miss the birth of the helpless podgy puppies.

They'd need someone to help care for them.

Zimbini

Seven months later, she did run away. To a pork farm about two miles down the track. She hid in a stall with a suckling mother and whispered to the ten piglets, 'It's my birthday.' The Child was six.

She stayed hidden on the farm for two days, her hair mingled with the straw as she snoozed, hid and watched the piglets.

Her birthday present was priceless: the pigs took a great interest in her.

But then she was spotted and driven home by two Afrikaans policemen who had breath like her mother's instant coffee.

As soon as she got home, she was taken by her father into her bedroom and belted across the backside several times. She didn't understand why her bum needed to be bare for this, and it seemed to take a long time.

The irony of being punished for running away by a father who clearly hadn't missed her was not lost on The Child.

After the spanking, her parents put her to bed and locked their bedroom door as usual. The animal sounds through the door were not dissimilar to the pigs in the sty. But, for some reason, these sounds did not make her happy.

Zintathu

Shortly after the pig farm incident, the parents took The Child on a trip to Lesotho. They stopped overnight in a ronde Vaal where she could hear the lions prowling around close-by as she tried to sleep. Her parents had gone to a dance at the hotel nearby, leaving her alone.

When she woke up in the middle of the night, she could still hear the low growls. She didn't know if she was frightened or glad of the company.

Next morning, they drove to Lesotho. Her parents giddy after the party.

Apparently, Mr Shoe Shoe was King of Lesotho. Her father wanted to talk to The King about diamonds. They had to climb up a big hill to find The King and when they reached his hut, they were all sweaty and breathless.

Her father was in one of his manic moods, thinking he could conquer this little land-locked country with his smarm offensive. His grin was alligator-wide and about as deep as a puddle. The Child hated those smiles. They usually preceded some bullshit.

King Shoe Shoe burst out of his home, like one of the charging rhinos The Child had seen at Kruger National Park. But no leathery skin, here, more like melting treacle.

The King stopped short, pufts of earth dust wafting up from his splayed bare feet. He stared intensely at the long blonde haired, china-blue eyed child. In that moment, the sun lit up his bonfire toffee skin and they were both suspended in a bubble of mutual fascination. Neither spoke.

Then he threw off the colourful cloak of his blanket and wailed at the sky something that sounded like, 'Oooh ley oh ooo ley lo… kea u rata, tanda lula!' He had very few clothes on underneath.

Next, his massive hands, a bracing corset around her little chest, grasped her and swooped her up way above his head. He threw her so high, she felt like she was in the clouds. Even though there weren't any in the sky that day.

When his mighty arms lowered The Child, her little heart rose like a loaf in the oven. For the first time, she felt what it was to be the apple of a man's eye. And life unexpectedly took a turn for the better.

And for the much, much worse.

Zine

Tanda Lula was in love with Mr Shoe Shoe. The Child now secretly called herself this because it's what Mr Shoe Shoe had shouted out in fascination and excitement when he saw her.

She had thrashed out an almighty tantrum when her parents wanted to leave Lesotho. Tanda Lula was going nowhere. She had finally found somewhere to belong. And someone to belong to.

The King had laughed. A laugh of plums and velvet and bears and chocolate. A natural laugh, so unlike her father's.

When her father had tried to get her into the car, she had pulled his hair and scratched his face. The alligator grin stayed perma-fixed in place. The eyes like mildewed concrete.

There would be trouble back in Cape Town. There'd be locked doors and silences that stretched over many sleeps. But The Child didn't care.

Mr Shoe Shoe had made her feel something she never knew existed. And she wanted to punish her father for not doing it sooner.

As they drove back to the suburban bungalow, The Child was planning ways to run away and make it back to Lesotho.

She would ask Mr Shoe Shoe to be her daddy.

Zintlanu

Running away on a normal day in her life would not have been difficult. Unfortunately for The Child, something happened that made it much trickier than usual.

It had begun as an ordinary day. Pronutra for breakfast, then playing on the sparse front 'lawn' of the corner bungalow.

She was wearing the purple hot pants her mother had made. Her mother was good at sewing and often sat in the lounge with colourful materials and her needles and threads – making something nice out of not much.

Today, Pamela the Schizophrenic sat at her mother's small bare feet as she sewed. Her mother had taken her into their home because she had nowhere else to go. Pamela always wore three pairs of trousers – at the same time. All corduroy. The Child did not know why. She also smelled funny and had long, greasy hair.

The Child, by contrast, had long, thick golden hair that she could sit on. The sunshine of South Africa had added highlights to her hair and freckles to her face. Big cornflower blue eyes stared out of this face, watching, always watching. Taking in the signals other people gave out and carelessly left behind. Feeling their secret poison, their snake-like ways and their trickery. Very early on, she'd seen that the dogs were easier to trust.

This morning, the dogs had run off together, to the back of the bungalow. Presumably to mate, as they sometimes did on the little hill at the back.

Tanda Lula was looking at her bicycle in the front drive, wondering if she should use it to run away to Mr Shoe Shoe. Just as she decided not to, a hunched Pamela came out of the bungalow through the open front door. She didn't speak to The Child but crept towards her, a whiff of mushrooms coming off the noisy corduroys.

The Child had watched hungry lionesses stalking springbok in the Kruger National Park. And, like those alert little creatures, she now sprang from standing to sprinting. Taking off up the street, bare footed, as the lunatic chased her. When The Child glanced back, she saw a glint in Pamela's eyes – and in her left hand.

After that, it was all a big blur. The neighbours. The bread knife. The police. Her parents arguing; 'Why the hell wasn't she checked out?', 'How the fuck did she get a knife?', 'What if she'd killed you?'

When they had run out of words, they went into the bedroom and locked the door.

Tanda Lula lay in bed, wondering what would have happened if Pamela had caught up with her before the neighbours stopped her.

Maybe all she'd wanted was a hug.

Zintandathu

Ever since then, her parents had watched her more closely. Her mother kept her in the kitchen, playing on the floor. They baked. Bright yellow lemons rolled around the floor. Mummy made pastry that melted in her mouth. Sticky meringue made alpine peaks in the Tupperware bowls.

But there were no more feral play fights with the German Shepherds. No more wild excursions into the mealy fields, sucky mud between her toes. No more African drums making her real heartbeat.

Her blood was black, she knew that. Not from the cancer that would eventually take her mother too early, but from the Africa that binds to your bones and clings on to the double helix of your DNA. Some get it, some don't.

She didn't need domestic imprisonment. Her soul needed to be swallowed whole by Africa. She had to find a way back to Mr Shoe Shoe who would squash her with delight like his very own daughter. She wanted that funny feeling in her tummy again – like a tiny spinning top in her belly button.

Instead, she had to breathe in the sickness of the bungalow-barbecue-white-life. The fake alligator grin. The embarrassing old persons' grunty noises. The accidental child living incidentally in a bubble-couple's life.

Days and days of being watched, but not seen, dragged on. Then, luckily, The Alligator did something bad and Mummy's attention whipped around, like a darting lighthouse beam; powered by the African heat and a strong belief in fairy tale princes.

Isixhenxe

'Dance for Lance, dance for Lance, dance for Lance', her mother's mocking voice turned The Child's raspberry jam sandwiches rancid. She picked up her Enid Blyton and read the words with the focus of a cat about to pounce on a mouse.

As her parents argued, Tanda Lula heard nothing but a pleasant buzzing in her ears. Every word was worshipped. Not just their meaning, but the way the letters looked together; the undulations and the incredible beauty of the black on white lines. This made her a slow reader but, since she was never without a book, she had still read hundreds of them between the ages of three and six. It was one thing her parents didn't starve her of.

She didn't understand what this current argument was about. 'Dance for Lance' didn't make any sense to her, although the anger in the atmosphere did. Her little body was frozen as her mind focussed on the storyline about lashings of ginger beer and George's loyal dog Timmy.

George claims to never ever tell lies because that's a cowardly thing to do. The Child agrees but has learned that telling the truth can make people mad. One reason why she watches more than she speaks.

Her mother has now gone from mocking to drinking. The Child can hear the cork being popped and the glugs splashing into the glass. She studies the words harder. The Alligator is grinning at a blonde woman on another picnic bench. The Child's peripheral vision has been honed by her introversion over the years. She glares at the letter 'G' in the middle of page 53. G, G, G, G, G. Gee-gee. A horse called Prince. A donkey called Dan. Soft muzzles. Kind faces.

In a world far, far away, a brittle wine glass is smashed.

Sisibhozo

Her cue was the clearing up of the shards. Suburban acquaintances, shining with schadenfreude, fell over each other to help. Both sexes formed a hunched circle with their backs to The Child. The men hoping to bed her mother while she was weepy and vulnerable. The women gleeful that the obsessed and tactile couple was disintegrating.

Cradling her Famous Five, Tanda Lula backed away into the bush. Her plan was to be adopted by Mr Shoe Shoe by teatime tomorrow. It would be her seventh birthday. The first step was to find a nice truck driver who was going from Cape Town to Durban. She knew that Lesotho was on the way to Durban and would ask to be a stowaway. She was sure they would be kind once she told them she was running away from an indifferent family to one that cared.

Once through the bush, Tanda Lula dawdled along the edge of the main road, hiding if she saw a car approaching, but waving if she saw a truck. After twenty minutes or so, a truck stopped. It was driven by a man called Timi, a Ugandan truck driver who was totally unaware that he was one of the first people to have contracted AIDS in Africa. In the years ahead he would pass on the disease to hundreds of prostitutes on his regular trucking route, all of them oblivious to the virus coursing through their blood. Fortunately, Timi was not interested in little girls. But he was very interested in the cash he could sell them for.

Shooing an outraged chicken off the dusty passenger seat, Timi asked, 'Wat is jou naam?' The Child looked far, far down the long road with her clear blue eyes. 'Tanda Lula', she said with some pride, though the words made a little catch in her small throat.

As the truck bounced and chugged along the pitted road, The Child explained in patchy Afrikaans that she had to get to Lesotho by tomorrow where The King, Mr Shoe Shoe, was to adopt her.

Timi kept his blood shot eyes on the road and nodded earnestly. His silence and cuddly shape were often mistaken for empathy and softness, while they really masked a complex Machiavellian mechanism. As the cogs turned, a variety of plans sprung into his mind.

When The Child woke up, the chicken was on her lap and the truck had stopped. It was dark outside and quite cool in the cabin. There was a pineapple on the floor, and she rested her foot on it. She remembered the layby and imagined it was her father's head, pressing harder with her foot and grinding it into the matting. The soles of her feet were thick skinned, and she felt no pain from the prickles.

Lithoba

She nearly fell out as the passenger door opened suddenly. The chicken squawked and flapped, fighting for balance, its claws digging into her little legs. The cabin light cast a glow on the shape-thing that had wrenched open the door – a tall, golden form like a lion standing on its hind legs but with no face.

'My, what big blue eyes you have.'

'What long blonde hair you have.'

The shape spoke. And, if the golden form had been bathed in a better light and she had seen the mouth that said these words, The Child would have noticed the familiar wide alligator grin and slate-hard eyes, and she may have screamed. This might have alerted the retired policeman who had just pulled up next to them at the rest stop. But, because of the darkness, the trust and the longing (as well as her regular lion dream), she smiled at the man and let him lift her down from the truck. And, so, a chain of events began that would change Tanda Lula, and Africa, for ever.

Timi counted his fistful of rand. Selling children was always lucrative. His mind was on steak dinners, whores and rifles. Not even a flash-thought of The Child's fate crossed his mind. As he drove off into the night, the chicken pecked at the squashed pineapple in the footwell.

'Thank you for taking me to Mr Shoe Shoe,' said The Child to the lion man. 'Of course, little princess, no problem.' He opened the back door of the Mercedes and ushered her in. 'Lie down and sleep, princess, it's a long, long way to Lesotho.' Tanda Lula got into foetal position and put her hands together in prayer as she always did. 'Thank you, heavenly Father God. Thank you, heavenly Father God,' she whispered to herself. She would soon be welcomed into the family of Mr Shoe Shoe, all warm with that wanted feeling.

The last thing she saw as she closed her eyes were some lacy red knickers, and a half full bottle of whiskey sloshing back and forth, behind the driver's seat.

A lion, the size of a VW Beetle, paced under the ironing-board-shaped African tree. Its paws – bigger than horses' hooves – scuffed up fluffy dust clouds. Back and forth, back and forth, until he caught a whiff of scent in the breeze. Just above his massive head, The Child hung on to the flimsy, bending branches. She was like a cast-iron Christmas bauble, a burden to the branch, that couldn't hope to be held up by the poor tree for long. It was just a matter of time until the branches bowed low and dropped her within striking distance of those paws. The lion knew this and almost smiled. Sniffing the air and biding his time. His prey would be sweeter for his patience. Sugar and spice and all things nice. Tanda Lula tried to move up the branch, out of harm's way but her movements just made the branches sag more. It was inevitable: the branches buckled, The Child fell, the lion went to strike.

A spilt second before she felt the scythe-like claw puncture her cheek, Tanda Lula woke up.

This was always the way in her lion tree dream. Her heart did the machine gun thing.

But, when she opened her eyes, everything was ok. The other lion in her life was staring at her between the front seats of the Mercedes. (Her 'father' had nearly called her Mercedes due to his lust for high end vehicles. In the end, the name her parents gave her was an insult, so she never used it. First, she saw herself as 'The Child', then Tanda Lula, then… later on, as 'Kween Tombi' – at last, a name given to her in love and wonder.)

'Alright, princess?' said the non-dreamy lion. 'Sleep ok? Eh, can you do me a favour, princess? Stay lying down, eh? We don't want anyone stopping your little adventure now do we?' The lion winked and sneered in one weird twitch. 'We'll be there in no time, princess. Timi said you've got The King of Lesotho waiting for you! Is that right, now?' The lion laughed and laughed until he coughed and coughed. His phlegmy retch merged with the splutter of the engine croaking to life. The Child closed her eyes and ears and opened her heart to God and prayed. The wheels turned. The whiskey bottle rolled.

(Note to readers: The chapter headings are in Xhosa. This is an extract of a novel.)

Runner-up

THE ROAD TO ITACUIAXA

by Clemily Martin

Sometimes, when plagued with fatigue, Yara's mother would forget her daughter was missing an arm. She would run her hands down her trunk, expecting a limb, a wrist, halting, never longer than a fraction of a second, as her tips met the soft stump of skin that folded into her daughter's left shoulder. This was one of those moments when, fuelled by the rush of adrenaline at the prospect of spending the night stranded in unknown lands, she forgot, and attempted to grab Yara by both arms to hurry her along the muddy road before nightfall.

Moments beforehand, Yara and her mother were sat on a thirteen-hour bus ride, which, had it not discharged its passengers mid-journey, would have taken them from Uacuto, a village in rural Bolivia from which they had been displaced, to Itacuiaxa, a town past the Brazilian border. It was an old, rattly bus, cramped with travellers of all kinds; along its narrow corridor, the humid summer air mingled with the smell of unwashed itinerant bodies and spread like steam in curling waves. Unable to sleep, Yara traced her fingernails over the armrest's decaying enamel, chipping at its edges. Eventually, her fingers fell limp and the cool of the newly exposed metal against her hot skin sent her to sleep. Thunder rumbled. The dry, cracked earth clumped under the gushing downpour and soon the road became thick with mud. The wheels struggled until the wailing engine gave in, still hours from the border. Shaken from slumber by his compromised safety, the driver chased the travellers off the bus as cattle, terrorizing them with the threat of ruthless border officers pouncing on the vehicle, a jackpot full of paperless vagabonds.

Thirty-odd wandering souls followed the road eastwards, struggling against the subsiding light. The crowd dissipated as the track lifted uphill and a few were lost to the false promises of half-lit suburban towns. Yara and her mother lagged behind, weighed down by the blankets, cloths, pans and tinned foods on their backs. They stopped under the flickering light of a roadside shack to dislodge the mud amassed under their soles. An old man approached, accompanied by a goat far better fed than himself. He knelt down and presented Yara with a carved tool.

'There is a tiny village, where the road curves in,' he explained, teaching her to scrape in downward motions to avoid mud spits, 'where settlers have thrashed a clearing among the trees and built their huts.'

Yara's mother signalled.

'My mother asks if the air is clear.'

'So clear it pierces your lungs. The cool morning air stays trapped beneath the canopy,' he replied, his sun-scorched cheeks glowing under the pale light. 'No one will bother you there,' he added, sensing the mother's uncertainty. 'Barely anyone knows it exists.'

Yara shook the clumps of mud off the tool and handed it back to the old man.

'Keep it,' he insisted. 'It will pour through the night.'

Three hours later and now accustomed to the darkness, Yara and her mother sidled along a narrowing path, lined with shrubs and feathered bushes, rustling in the breeze. They delved into the forest, zigzagging over the exposed, sprawling tree roots. When they reached an opening above which floated about a dozen pointed straw tops, Yara fetched a few stray branches while her mother fumbled for the blankets. They set up a makeshift tent and fell asleep under half-draped cloths, their stiff, worn-out bodies already softening and moulding into the dips and ridges of the uneven forest floor.

Morning light flooded through the gaps in the tent and woke them up, offering their first glimpse of the glossy, meandering canopy. They emerged, brushing the dirt off their clothes, and were met by a double dozen languid faces, still sunken in sleep, turning to face them in the slowest imaginable rotation, as if burdened by the weight of their skulls. They sat outside their thatched huts, slumped over tree stumps with outstretched legs and cupped backs, busying their idle hands shelling nuts and snapping sticks into piles over crispy scorched leaves.

Their eyes, fixated far into the distance, were completely glazed over, rendered almost translucent by a blue-grey glutinous liquid which coated their dark pupils. They were sucking on the same sticks they were snapping, mechanically chewing just as slowly as they had rotated their heads moments earlier; a pace so far removed from the bustle of the world from which Yara and her mother had come. As their jaws opened and closed, the sticks softened and released a thick black sap which exuded from their mouths, staining their lips, revealing missing teeth and blackened gums. Yara's mouth gaped open. It was as if time itself, in this sheltered clearing, had surrendered its ticks to the sticky, clicking sounds of mastication. The girl quickly bowed her head so as not to betray her disarray. She spotted streams of creamy maggots crawling restless in all directions, pursuing her ankles, perusing her mother's sandals and contorting in and out of the gaps between the hut-dwellers' toes, as if these too, stiffened by years of immobility, had become part of the fabric of the forest floor. A few lost birds cawed as they circled above the canopy, half-heartedly calling out to any iridescent-winged friends skirting the skies.

Yara's mother was struck by the sight of such desolation, discomforted by the mix of fear and repugnance materialising in her body. She hastily packed up the tent and drove her daughter out of the clearing, the same way they had come the night before. Yara trailed behind, riding up and down the protruding tree roots, appeased by the quiet of these inhabitants, living on the periphery of a noisy world, unphased by their arrival or the maggots lacing their feet. Without fully understanding the feelings amassing in her young heart, she began to develop a peculiar yearning for the contentment of the hut-dwellers, for their need for nothing more than what they already had. Yara and her mother were out of the rainforest and back on the dirt road by noon, as if they had never arrived.

By late afternoon, they were already on a cross-border sleeper train to Amapaia, a small town just past the Brazilian border, from which they planned to move eastwards to reach Itacuiaxa. Unprepared for any extra spendings following the mud-stuck bus ride, the two lay outstretched on the curved roof of a mid-train carriage. Yara breathed in as the cool air blew off the beads of moisture that had collected above her lip, reminded of the many summer nights she had spent waiting while her mother sneaked out to the neighbouring valley, loading handfuls of plump goldenberries in her upturned skirt. There too, the cool wind had brushed over her face, tickling her lashes under the timid stars as she cradled her brother in cotton blankets. Though the breeze here was less sweet perhaps, for now they were only two.

Once the train had picked up all the overnight passengers, the pair climbed down from the roof and slipped into an empty sleeper carriage with two made-up bunks, just as the evening showers broke, warmed by the day's heat on their way down. Yara followed the beads of water hurling at the window beside her cheek, travelling jaggedly along the dirty pane, stopping and starting and occasionally coalescing into larger droplets, as if copulating in ecstasy at the random nature of chance encounters.

The mother reached into her basket and tore off two pieces of sweet bread. She pulled out a jar of dark red guava paste which she had bought in a dimly-lit village shop not far from the station; a sure sign, she had thought, that they were nearing the border. Yara's eyes lit up as she discovered this mysterious jelly, watching impatiently as her mother's fingertips pressed the paste into the pieces of fluffy bread. Yara gasped as she remembered something she had forgotten. From the well-worn pocket of her yellow sundress, she removed a perfectly shelled, smooth boiled egg, whiter than any shade of food she had tasted before. Her mother's eyes lit up in turn, half-amazed, half-confounded, for she did not remember paying for this little egg at the village shop. Yara's shy smile revealed the covert sacrifice she had made while her mother stood at the counter, anxiously counting up coins under the watchful eye of the shopkeeper. Moved by the simplicity of this milky egg, held out so gracefully by such a small, gentle palm, the mother resisted frowning in reprimand. Instead, she smiled at her daughter's mischief and they both broke out into quiet, complicit laughter at the excitement of the meal to come.

The jelly and the yolk formed a paste so thick in Yara's mouth it cracked in segments over her tongue. She kept it lodged there at each new bite, pulling her dimples in as she savoured the mixture of sweet, tangy and buttery flavours. The pair fell asleep, exhausted, on the same bunk. As the girl's mind gathered its moments of respite, she dreamt of the satin-ridged maggots of the rainforest, crawling up her narrow legs and suddenly metamorphosing into swarms of large sticky flies, flying clumsily past her eardrums. Her body shuddered and landed on something warm and soft, as the train pulled into Amapaia. And, for the first time in what must have been seven years, Yara woke up in her mother's arms.

They scuttled off the train, mixing with the crowds so as not to arouse suspicion. Outside the station, they imbibed the melancholy hum of long, drawn-out vowels flooding the country's language, a sound so familiar to their wistful hearts and yet so distinct from the melodies of their own mother tongue. They followed the signs to the town centre, pinned to orange-budded trees pricking the clear blue sky, hoping to find somewhere to refill their gourds.

The town was filled with the smell of freshly bleached cotton, hanging diagonally from window to window over the grey cobblestones. Beyond the washing lines, market-goers crowded the streets between stalls, chattering noisily, fondling foods and haggling prices. No more than two foods were being sold: dried salted codfish, hung in batches, and a round, pale yellow fruit, the size of a small melon, piled high in wooden crates. A vendor in rugged overalls caught Yara eyeing up the abundance of smooth, waxy orbs and invited her to approach.

'Po-me-lo,' he enunciated, slicing one of the orbs in half, revealing an even paler, translucent inside.

Yara looked down at the exposed core, with its hundreds of ridged capsules enveloped in a thick white pith, about twice as thick as the pulp.

'Here,' he said, carving out a few segments and dipping them in a pot of cane sugar.

He handed them over in a paper cone for Yara to try, exposing his blackened fingernails, dripping in juice. The sugar-crusted pieces looked to her like candied jewels, glistening like the gems she had glimpsed through pawnshop windows, in the spaces between the curvaceous silhouettes of widows draped in black lace mourning veils. Yara followed her mother into a dark-wooded tavern and waited by the door, a few crystals still hanging loosely at the corners of her mouth. A man was sitting on a stool at the window, staring blankly at the men and women walking back from the market with handfuls of fruit and fish for the week.

'Tap water? And no table service?' cackled the waiter in disbelief, shooing away the mother with a single flapping hand. 'This is no place for beggar women,' he said smirking, resting his elbow on a shiny metal tap behind the counter.

The man at the window stood up from his stool in protestation, but before he could say a word, Yara and her mother were back in the street, speedily marching away. Gripped tight under her mother's pit, Yara looked down at her shy, unsupported breasts creasing the cotton of her outgrown sundress and wondered how the waiter knew they would not be sitting down to eat. They stopped in their tracks as the man from the window cried out scampering behind them, clutching three rock-hard salted cods in his right hand. He clumsily offered them some water from his home, a short walk away beyond the marshes.

They followed the man through the bowing reeds which whispered as they brushed against their exposed knees, bleeding for human affection. Puzzled by the ease with which they accepted the man's invitation, Yara recalled a line her mother had spoken years ago: *suspicion is a luxury which travellers like us cannot afford.* And, allayed by the man's strong hands swaying along his frame as he graciously skirted the marshy puddles, without much further thought, Yara's trust began to grow.

Above a run-down tobacco shop selling used children's toys, there was a small room, built into the roof with sloping windows, overlooking the cloudless sky. A mezzanine supported an old single mattress and on the lower level, there were two chairs, a three-legged table and a kitchenette. The man invited them to sit and filled two plastic goblets with water from the tap. He gestured to the mother and they engaged in silent conversation for several minutes, smiling and nodding at each other knowingly, as if they had met once before. Yara's mother went to lie down on a straw mat below the mezzanine.

'Why does everyone eat pomelos?' Yara asked.

'It's the only fruit still growing in these parts,' replied the man.

'And why is the skin so thick and the fruit so small?'

'Protection.'

The man reached up to a buckling shelf above the sink, stacked high with dozens of jars filled with a pale yellow liquid.

'This is what we do with all the pomelos,' he explained.

He opened a jar and provided Yara with a spoon speckled with rust. She dug it in, swirling through the thick gel.

'How did you know my mother was mute?' she probed, spooning a large mass of jam into her mouth.

'Because she reminded me of mine.'

Yara paused. 'What is your name?'

'Nino.'

Nino went to rest on his mattress. Now alone in the kitchenette, Yara fetched one of the scooped-out pomelo halves by the sink and pressed her back into the chair. She tucked the waxy dome under her dress and set it over her stomach, reminded that her mother too would have once carried a similar pomelo-sized orb in her belly. Yara rested her eyes for a moment, picturing her mother lying safe on Nino's mat with her hand outstretched, the same hand that had, for the past twelve years, guided her through the rivers, the reeds, the rain, the marshes, the heat, the burns, the blisters and the sleepless nights spent crossing borders and bridges. As she sat motionless, moved to tears by her mother's immeasurable strength, Yara dreamt she was a baby again, cupped in her mother's palm and laid to sleep in the curved membrane of a pomelo skin, sealed shut from the world in this protective orb and returned to her mother's belly. She dreamt her life started all over again, growing there, feeding day after day on the sugary syrup made by the man with the large palms.

As Yara's eyes opened and narrowed their focus, she saw a shape flash past the length of the kitchenette. A tiny, trembling mouse froze in mid-sprint, assessing its safety under the raised cupboard. How much better could Itacuiaxa possibly be, Yara asked herself, sitting in this sky-lit room, surrounded by thirty-six pots of pomelo jam, as Nino and her mother fell asleep to the quiet rumble of the half-broken fridge. For the first time in as long as she could remember, she was overwhelmed by a sense of peace; and hoped, if Nino consented, that her mother would let them stay there for a while longer, before setting off again. Under the sun's dawdling evening rays and the keen eye of her new whiskered friend, Yara wondered how many more nights they would spend like this, without the world ever knowing where they were.

Third Place

AUTOMATIC

by Alison Targett

Joyce grips the smooth steering wheel of her beloved Audi S5 Cabriolet as she takes the slip road on to the M25. The sleek blue convertible is one of the two joys in her life since her husband died eight years earlier.

She loves its acceleration. She loves its shape. She loves the fact she opted for an automatic – so much easier – and she loves that she can open the roof with the flick of a switch allowing the air to rush through her long grey hair. It is exhilarating. With her sunglasses on, no-one would ever guess she is 77.

Her other joy is spending time with her grandsons. And that is where she is heading today – just like every Wednesday. From 11am until the evening, she will look after those beautiful toddlers. Oh how they are always so pleased to see her! How precious they are to her! Recently, her daughter insisted that Joyce stay overnight. Beth says it gives her and her husband a chance to nip out for dinner, a little bit of 'us' time as she puts it – as well as a couple of extra hours with her Mum.

Joyce knows that Beth's insistence has little to do with 'us' time, but more to do with her daughter's belief that her mother should no longer drive in the dark. So, there was that one occasion when she forgot her distance night-driving glasses and the journey home took her twice the time. She didn't dare go over 40 miles per hour all the way. Forgetting the glasses was just an oversight.

Joyce eases the steering wheel to the left now, as the slip road inclines towards the main M25 carriageway. There is nothing wrong with her driving, she thinks, and presses her foot harder on the accelerator. She loves the satisfying sound of the gearbox as it moves up to third gear and she feels the surge of power under her foot. She indicates right and swings across the first lane and in to the second of the four-lane highway. She feels in control. A car pulls ahead of her on the right. Red, expensive, fast. Joyce chances a look at the driver. Boy racer, she thinks – no older than 40 – and she smiles. Her foot depresses the accelerator a little further; the gearbox moves up to fourth. The engine roars.

In the tiny boot of her Audi, Joyce has her overnight bag. She doesn't want to stay tonight – the nights are getting lighter now and she likes her own bed. Beth and her husband are not even planning on going out this evening. Instead, they are going to cook Joyce a meal and have a glass or two of wine with her. They want to have 'a chat' about something. Joyce knows already what it is, but she doesn't want to think about it. It makes her feel angry and unsettled; quite powerless. What happened in that town centre car park last week was nothing. Really nothing at all. It was a fault with the car. She is sure of it.

But the police were involved, her daughter had shouted. Yes, shouted! And someone could have been killed! She and Beth had always had an easy relationship, but this moment on the phone a week ago, almost drove Joyce to scream 'Leave me alone!' and slam down the receiver. She hadn't because it was her daughter and the mother of the two precious cherubs whose faces gave her reason to live. She acknowledged Beth's concern, mumbled something about how everyone commented on what a safe driver she was, said something further about driving being her independence. Without it she would just be marooned in suburbia, reliant on erratic bus services and taxis.

However, Joyce knows that while Beth let the subject drop that day, it is very much top of the agenda for tonight's overnight stay.

Joyce shuffles in her seat, releases the seat belt for a moment to find a more comfortable position. The annoying warning alarm beeps and Joyce says out loud, 'All right, all right,' before clunking the belt back into place.

Privately, she has done a lot of thinking about what happened the week before, but she is still puzzled. And there have been a couple of nights when she has woken up feeling cold and then clammy as her mind processes those blurred events into vivid nightmare. The police were so kind to her, particularly the young woman constable who wrapped a foil sheet around her and gave her hot tea with sugar. 'For the shock,' she said as she pushed the steaming cup towards Joyce in a local café.

She told the policewoman how one minute she was sitting in her Audi in the car park and the next, as she put the gearstick in to 'drive' with her foot on the brake, the car had quite literally shot over a curb, then another and ended up bonnet-first in a hedge. Fortunately, it was a quiet time of day and the car park had been almost empty. There were scratches on the bonnet and dents on the underside of the bumper where it had hit the curbs. But no other damage. You were very lucky, the policewoman said. An hour earlier and that car park had been full of mothers with prams and young children. There's a nursery tucked away in the corner there, the policewoman added and looked down at the table. Then she looked back up at Joyce. Did she think she might have mistaken the accelerator for the brake, she asked gently. Joyce actually laughed at that moment. 'Goodness, no!' she said. 'There are only two pedals. I would never do such a silly thing.'

She was given a caution by the lovely constable and allowed to go home. She assured the policewoman that she would have the car's electrics checked out at her local garage. She rang immediately but the earliest they could see her was next week. The dents and scratches couldn't be fixed until two weeks after that. Anyway, the car is running quite smoothly again now.

The gearbox gives a little jolt and moves up to fifth gear. Joyce pulls the car over to the third lane. If she keeps up this speed, she will be at her daughter's house within half an hour. Those two little boys will be waiting at the door. She can hear their chirruping voices now. She smiles. 'Granny's here! Granny's here!' they would chorus, triggering that same elated feeling she has every week when their eyes meet hers. Looking after her grandsons is exhausting, but they make her feel alive. They make her feel loved.

The Audi starts to close the distance between Joyce and a white flatbed truck ahead of her. Old pieces of furniture are tethered down with rope to the truck's battered sides. The remnants of someone's home, someone's life. As the Audi edges nearer, Joyce can see a large wardrobe with a single mirrored door strapped to the back of the driver's cabin. How that brings back memories! She had one just like that when she was a child. It seemed so big to her back then that she would often climb inside to play imaginary games. And suddenly she is there: she can smell the wood polish, she can almost hear the squeak of the door's heavy hinges and the rattle of the hangers. Joyce feels for a moment like she is stepping back into her own childhood. If she reaches out now, perhaps she could touch the dolls lined up inside, run her fingers down the fabric of her dresses. And there is bright summer sunlight. So rich it is almost red.

She can see her own reflection in the mirrored door ahead now. Instead of grey hair, she sees golden locks, pigtails and ribbons. The red glow becomes so deep, so close that she senses its warmth wrapping around her. Then she puts her foot on the brake and her reflection shatters in to a million pieces.

Fourth Place

CHAPTER 1 – THE WAITING ROOM

by Ricky Cibardo

It wasn't clear to me whether the light I was headed towards was supposed to be so bloody bright or maybe the months I'd spent in darkness had obliterated my sensitivity to the beaming rays of multi-colour.

Bright white light, it certainly wasn't, I wondered if my life's emotions represented each colour that flew nonchalantly into every part of my formerly lifeless body.

What felt like the back catalogue of Stevie Wonder's greatest hits played loudly in the background in an unapologetic manner as I started to contemplate what was waiting for me, if and when I finally docked from the river of dreams, except I wasn't waking up from this one.

I checked if I could touch the sides. Nope, doesn't seem to be any sides, my fingers just waved through the coloured lights like a knife through butter.

For some reason, I kept checking behind me for my family. Force of habit, I guess. I know they were there with me at the hospital. I could hear them talking to me. Funny how I would have died to hear some of those beautiful words that they spoke to me whilst I was conscious. Well, I suppose I did die, just would have rather heard them when I was alive. Feel a massive sense of guilt for taking them all for granted. Wonder if they knew that I said my goodbyes?

I couldn't speak but I am sure they would have known.

The journey to wherever I was going was taking a while. Was I supposed to be enjoying the view or taking in my surroundings? I know that I can feel a massive comfort, even a sense of peacefulness. I always assumed I would be balling my eyes out at this stage.

I felt cold, then hot and then back cold again. My instant reaction was to cover up but I am not even sure if my flushes were due to the temperature or a sudden panic of the unknown.

Rather annoyingly, halfway through Stevie's harmonica interlude to *For Once in my Life* his *Songs in the Key of Life* abruptly, however somewhat ironically, died.

The multi-colours swiftly disbanded and collected themselves again to form a guard of honour, circulating around the pink arched doorway. Angels, that looked more like extras in a poor adaption of Star Wars, flanked two plump men with clipboards. I only knew they were angels because of the pink glittery letters plastered to their ageing wings spelling out A.N.G.E.L like they were sporting their favourite football player on a replica shirt.

The angel standing closest to the end of the guard of honour beckoned me to come towards her. It felt like I was about to be asked for identification, but alas, I was butt naked and feeling rather vulnerable and my lack of pockets to hold any kind of proof of age was shamefully evident.

'Name?' the angel I now know as Clara from her tatty name badge, rather angrily, demanded

'Jacob Jones at your service sweetheart.' I have never said 'sweetheart' in my entire life but to be fair this wasn't a normal situation for me.

Clara looked inquisitively over her clipboard that she had hastily snatched from one of the men standing rather menacingly next to her. She had a look of someone who had heard every line before but was too weary to take me down with a one liner of some kind.

'Well we know why you are here, and we know when Jake had to leave to get you, as you disturbed his break but what I don't know is where you are going next.'

It seemed a very well-rehearsed script that Clara just read out, well apart from, 'Who the bloody hell is Jake?!'

Clara whispered to her angel friend stood next to her and with that the shyer version of Clara apologetically hollered into her walkie talkie.

'Jake, you back yet?'

Clara recoiled backwards with a smile in what I can only guess was embarrassment that they had disturbed Jake again but with satisfaction that it wasn't her who did it this time.

'Yep, be there in two Sarah,' came the muffled reply of a man who was clearly halfway through chomping something tasty.

The plump men disappeared into the abyss at the same time a man of slim stature, maybe 5'6" in height ambled over with no great purpose.

'What's up Sarah?' Jake spoke in a cockney voice but with a hint of west country accent.

'This gentleman wants to know who you are.'

'Did you tell him that we've already met?'

'No Jake, sorry Jake.'

'Oh hello, I am just here, you can speak to me,' I retorted, rather put off that they weren't even looking at me.

I was starting to get a bit miffed with the goings on now and by the look of the plastic, toy shop looking scythe Jake held on to with the air of a man that thought he was holding Excalibur, I kind of already knew who Jake was.

'It's simple squire, you have expired. If you're next question is 'Did I take your Soul?' then the answer is no, everyone asks that, it's all a load of baloney, I don't take souls, I just have to give you a nudge into your life reel.'

'Life reel?'

'Yeah, that bloomin' great, colourful, musical tube you just entered. Can't get in there without a little old push from me.'

'So, you go down below every time someone is about to die?'

'Yeah, sometimes I have some unexpected jobs when I am down there. Paperwork is a killer when you've not got an appointment booked in. Oops, sorry wrong choice of words. Still you're here now, anything I can do for you, just ask.'

With that, Jake turned and went back to wherever he came from.

Clara watched Jake go and once out of eyeshot she looked back at me and without hesitation, demanded, 'Take a seat through the smoke over there. You'll find some clothes to wrap around you and a drink. Food will be served around 7pm and at some point, Rocco will come out of Helleven and give you the heads up.'

I had more questions that I am sure Clara wasn't willing to answer so I cut my losses and kept quiet and proceeded towards the smoke. It was like a scene from that programme on TV where members of the public mimic their idols and sing, although I wasn't sure who I would turn into on the other side of the smoke.

Walking through the smoke was the most underwhelming experience.

I probably could have walked around it and ended up in the same place in the same amount of time.

I stopped on the yellow marker laid out with perfect symmetry below the open door.

The sign above the door, in Comic Sans font, read

ONCE YOU ENTER, YOU CANNOT RETURN

Moot point really, I am sure that I had already died and if books and random fantasists are to be believed, squeezing back down the tunnel had never been referenced.

As I walked through the open door, one of the plump men from earlier, now known to me as Billy due to a large tattered, embroidered badge on the lapel of his oversized bomber jacket, shouted over to me.

'Glad rags over 'ere mate.'

They were hardly glad rags, but I got the sentiment so walked over and picked up some loosely fitting trousers and a shirt with my name freshly printed with iron-on transfer and put them on.

'Grab a water and take a seat,' Billy murmured whilst looking me up and down.

The seating area was decked out with reclining chairs, large wooden tables and a TV. My first thought was that someone had just popped to IKEA and grabbed a load of flat packs but by the look of the four individuals reclined and half asleep, no such spontaneity had taken place very recently.

As customary in these situations, I checked that nobody was using the chair nearest the TV and sat down. In fact, I took being completely ignored as an invitation to take whatever seat I wanted and that one was better than any I supposed.

The silence was deafening, and it was only at this point that I had a sudden realisation that I didn't have a clue where I was or what was happening. All I knew was that some creature named Rocco would address me at some point and that maybe he had a penchant for Stevie Wonder.

'You'll find the remote underneath your chair mate,' came a voice from behind me.

'I'm Jamie, I died of a heart attack, been here a few weeks, don't eat the paella, it tastes like the hospital meals I was eating before I came here.'

'Pleasure to make acquaintance Jamie, my name is Jacob.'

'What did you die of Jacob?'

'I really don't know Jamie but thanks for confirming that I have actually died.'

'Ah, you are a Pobble Jacob.'

'What's a Pobble?'

'A Pobble is someone that has to wait to find out how they died as they still haven't decided down there.'

Jamie leaned back on his chair and motioned to me to do the same.

I began to think about my last days down below and for the life of me I couldn't remember anything about the time before I got taken by Jake. I distinctly have memories of saying goodbye to my family and heading to the office, but I don't remember getting there.

'You were covered in blood Jacob,' Jamie whispered into my ear, startling me into standing. 'Proper pool of blood you were in. All yours though. Loads of paramedics and police cars flying about. Mick and I enjoyed watching that one, knew that it would only be a matter of time before we met.'

'You must have seen what happened to me?' I demanded, not really paying attention to the other question I should have asked first of how they actually knew.

'No mate. Look up,' Jamie moved his head in the direction of the TV.

'What, you think we watch SKY TV on that box? Nah, we see what you look like before you get nudged by Jake on these TV's. Bloody, very bloody. I remember saying to Lexy, she's the fit girl in the yellow chair over by the flowers, that I reckon you were murdered, wasn't no natural causes.'

I stopped Jamie before he went on. Not because I didn't want to know any more detail, but a chill had just come over my newly, chaffing clothing. Everyone else in the room, sat bolt upright on the chairs, adjusting the pull-out trigger at the side of their recliners, looking intently in front of them.

The oxygen in the room seemed to disintegrate and the black shadow of a beast loomed over me as I sank down into my recliner. As I looked upwards, a creature that looked like his human head had been replaced with an Aardvark's head and opened his snout to speak; 'I'm Rocco and you are going to do as I say from this point onwards.'

THE BIG 5-OH!

by Lisa Barrett

12th August 2017 – 9am

'Today could be the best day of your life, mum.'

'Aw, thank you son.'

I levered the top half of my body off the mattress to catch a quick kiss on cheek from my gorgeous boy before he left the room. The girls had rushed out just before him, excitedly chatting about who was going to do my hair and makeup and John had gone off to make me a cup of coffee. I thought about the earlier call with mum and dad and felt a bit choked that they wouldn't be with me on my special birthday, but I understood – flights from Spain were expensive at this time of year.

Plonking back down on the bed, I looked at the carnage left behind after our family tradition of bundling into the bed of the birthday girl or boy. It always descended into fits of giggles and teasing about 'morning breath' with jokey sibling rivalry and mock-arguing over who was the favourite child. Today happened to be my 50th birthday we were celebrating.

I couldn't get my head around the fact that I was now fifty. No longer 'forty-something', a term I'd clung on to in my late 40s as I felt it kept things nicely open – implying I could've just turned 40 for all people knew – closer to 40 than 50.

I was surrounded by crumpled wrapping paper that needed sorting out – an uber-feminine selection of sugary pink, glittery and floral patterns embossed with hearts – a bit how I imagined a pile of unicorn vomit would look. I carefully put the bows and ribbons into a plastic bag and used a birthday card to scrape up shiny bits of gold plastic, shaped into champagne glasses. I felt guilty at how un eco-friendly it was and it took ages to clear up. Funny how the kids and John escaped before they could be chivvied into helping clear away the remnants of my birthday morning jubilee. Typical.

'Happy birthday to me…happy birthday to me…' I sang as I got on with tidying up. To be honest, I was pleasantly surprised that they'd managed to focus on me for a whole hour that morning without checking their phones. A mobile-free family gathering, no matter how short, was rarely without interruptions from pings and buzzes or some kind of 'wait-mum-I-just-have-to-check-this' alert. I even got undivided attention from my youngest and most mobile-dependent, Lily – TikTok addict and selfie extraordinaire. That said, she did manage to get a lovely 'boomerang' of me for Instagram, looking half decent. It's amazing what a puppy ears filter can do for a frazzled complexion.

I couldn't see any more confetti bits around the duvet, but wouldn't be surprised if I woke up the next day with a few rogue shiny bits stuck to my face – or maybe somewhere more uncomfortable. I smiled, thinking of those little gold shapes lodged into my wrinkles – an ironic celebration of my skin getting older and saggier. Happy birthday crinkle face!

Best day of my life? Will's words played in my head. Bless him. It was a really sweet thing to say, but turning 50 hardly amounts to the best day of your life, does it? I wasn't being ungrateful thinking this – I couldn't wait to celebrate my big birthday with my loved ones. But really, for it to be 'the best day of my life' I'd have to have woken up to find out I'd won millions on the lottery or that I'd entered some kind of time machine and turned 21 again. Imagine: no responsibility, no love handles or increasingly creaky joints. I mean, every day is the best day of your life at 21, isn't it?

Tidying up done, I fingered the summery dress hanging outside the wardrobe. I'd bought it from Whistles and it was one of those scarce meant-to-be finds. I'd been planning on wearing a pair of white jeans and a bright top with wedges to my party, but at the eleventh hour, decided I needed to find something a little more 'it's MY party'. Plus, thickening middle age spread and thigh flesh that seemed to be getting more dimples than a pre-school classroom, were not doing those white jeans any favours.

The clearing up took longer than expected so languishing in the bath wasn't to be – a quick shower that went tepid before I could wash the conditioner out of my hair had to suffice. How many times had we told

John that something had to be done about that blooming shower? A cold shower did nothing for my mood but it did make my boobs look pretty perky for all of 5 minutes – before room temperature hit and they went back to their original embonpoint which, at best, resembled empty little bean bags. The joys of middle age.

Padding across the landing, wrapped in a towel and desperately trying not to shout out 'fecking cold shower again, John!' I stumbled over the pile of makeup the girls had laid at my bedroom door. Sensible place to put it.

'Careful mum – that's my best Bobbi Brown highlighter!' shouted Lily.

'Oh, sorry Love.' I trilled, when I really wanted to shout, 'stupid bloody place to leave it then, isn't it?' but I quickly altered my gait just in time, so that I wouldn't smash it under my feet and hopped onto the bed, hoping the towel would stay fastened. Wouldn't want Will catching sight of his dear old mum's wobbly arse – that'd be enough to give anyone PTSD for life.

Once Aimee had expertly styled my usually wayward hair into smooth, natural-looking curls, it was time for makeup. I begged the girls to let me do it myself – I've had years of experience with my face, after all, and I don't do a bad job of slapping it on in 5 minutes – 10 if I'm off somewhere fancy. But the girls were having none of it. 'No mum. You never accentuate your eyes enough – look at your fabulous brows – they definitely need defining. Don't peek. You can look when we've finished.' I sat back and did as I was told. After all, Aimee, with typical traits of the eldest child, had been bossy since birth. And with Lily's addiction to YouTube tutorials leading to incredible knack of altering her facial features to suit the aesthetic trend of the moment – you'd think she'd been born with a contour palette and makeup brush in her hand – I hoped I'd be safe letting them loose on me.

The girls got on with it: mixing and matching foundations and tinted moisturisers, highlighting and bronzing my face. Then lifting up my crepey eyelids to draw eyeliner on the upper lid. 'Oh no – not too heavy,' I pleaded. 'Please babe – you know I'm not keen on my eyes being too done – it settles in the creases and make them look smaller.'

'Oh mum, be quiet! It looks lovely.'

'Yes mum, you look lovely,' agreed Lily, holding a little brown compact, eager to get to my brows and do that thing only youngsters can do so well – which is give you brows like black caterpillars sliming their way across your face.

'Help.' I thought. But I stayed quiet and allowed my droopy face to be hoiked, poked and painted.

Soon, it was time for the big reveal. 'Ta-da!' Aimee and Lily shouted in unison, pulling the mirror around to face me. I blinked furiously, trying to open my eyes under all that eyeshadow, then squinted…was that really me? Oh. Wow. I was expecting something resembling a grotesque hybrid granny/baby face, but I must say that, apart from the lines around the eyes looking slightly cakey, the girls had done a really good job of making my hair and makeup look suitably party-ready and fashionable without looking muttony. I reckoned I could easily pass for 48 and a half. The girls were glowing at my happiness as I cuddled them both and thanked them for giving their mummy a perfect birthday makeover!

Lunch with 'the girls' 2pm

There we all were. Nine of my loveliest friends beamed at me behind a bunch of pale pink balloons which were nestled among the biggest, shiniest, gold 5 and 0 shaped balloons I'd ever seen. There's no denying they looked very pretty floating up from the table and bobbing around like huge space ships – but did the whole world really need to know my age?

I looked at the women excitedly talking over each other and rummaging in their bags to get out presents. These were the beautiful, middle-aged, life-savers who have been with me through the ups and downs at various stages of my life. I felt unexpectedly teary as a huge cheer of 'Mrs B's fifty!' went up and I slipped into the seat next to my oldest friend Shelly and gratefully took the long-stemmed glass of champagne she proffered. Her pale blue eyes crinkled at the corners and that familiar mega-watt smile shined as she hugged me. We'd met aged four playing outside in our cul de sac – in the days when kids were out until dusk on their bikes and fell out of trees, breaking bones without their parents suing the local council. My big sister was among my friends too – well, she was the first female friend I ever had. I could hear her laughing, telling my dog-walking buddy and daily confidante, Jane, that it didn't seem possible her baby sister was fifty. 'You're telling me,' I thought. I still get a shock when I look in the mirror to see yet another grey hair has sprouted and wondering whether I'd always had that peach fuzz moustache or was that – once again – another wonderful sign of getting old?

An hour on, the bubbles were going down well and I finally started to feel myself relax a little. I was looking forward to six o'clock when John, the kids and the other guests would turn up. We'd hired a private room here in the pub, which had a lovely patio area we could spill out onto and drink, eat and dance the night away. I was so pleased the sun was shining and remembered how my dad used to tell me that he'd ordered the sunshine especially for my birthday and I'd believed him. Of course, as I got older, I realised that having a birthday on the glorious 12th of August, there was quite a high chance of a positive weather prediction.

Listening to the laughter and chattering around the table, I suddenly started to sense a feeling of slight anxiousness among a few friends. What on earth were they all doing on their phones? And blimey, how many times did Melisa need the loo? I knew we were ladies of a certain age and yes, once that Prosecco seal popped, it was hard to stop, but she'd literally been up and down like a yo-yo.

'Okay, can four of you make your way into the car outside please,' shouted my friend Liz across the table as the women began to discuss who was leaving and who would wait here until the next car came…

I had no idea what was going on but the friends that got up to go just blew me smiley kisses as they left. It seemed nobody was listening to my nervy demand to tell me what on earth was happening. Even though I knew 'my ladies' would never do anything to upset me – especially on my birthday – I was baffled and couldn't think of any reason at all that one by one, my mates were all leaving the restaurant. When my old schoolfriend Mary shouted out 'Hope you've got nice undies on Lis…' with a wink as she left the restaurant, I almost lost it. 'Oh no!' I wailed. Please someone tell me what is going on…'

Then there were just 4 of us left at the table. I looked at them one by one and said, 'Please don't let it be a stripper-gram or anything embarrassing. I'll never forgive you.' I think for the first time in my life, I honestly didn't have a clue – and couldn't conjure up any idea – about what was going on. To their credit, my sister, Jane and Liz were looking a bit sheepish.

'It's lovely. We promise. It's nothing that you won't like. It's going to be fine.' Liz smiled. Feeling mildly less anxious, I thought that maybe it was a kind of spa treat – mani-pedi – then dash back to the party. But – would my friends really interrupt a few hours of drinking and gossiping to go to a beauty salon? I didn't really think so. So, what was bloody going on?

'Ok, our turn now Lis. Come on…' said my sister as she stood up and held my hand to take me outside to the awaiting car. There was my friend Jane's husband, Andrew, in his new Porsche – 'I'm your designated driver, Madam,' he smiled. I realised that now I just had to go with it and was pleased that at least wherever we were going, we were going in style.

'Will we be back in time for the party…for when everyone else arrives?' The girls reassured me it was all going to be okay. 'Trust them,' my mind kept saying. I had no other bloody option really, but I imagining making my escape at the next set of red lights to jump on an E3 bus back home, getting into bed and hiding under the covers until this weird moment in my life was over. I didn't know if I liked being 50. At that moment, I just wanted to go back to the pub and drink – lots.

'Okay Lis, have a look at this.' From the front of the car, Jane had turned around to hold her phone in front of my face while my sister squeezed my hand. A video started and John came on the screen wearing exactly what he'd had on that morning. I scrunched my eyes to get a closer look and realised he was videoing from outside the pub we'd just left.

'Hi babe. Happy birthday. I hope by now you've had a few drinks, feel relaxed and are enjoying yourself. I just want to let you know that I thought really hard about what I could get you for your special birthday that would mean something. I thought, what is the one thing Lisa has always wanted? And then it came to me. I knew. But babe, before I am able to give you this thing, I need to know something…'

What was he doing...? I was trembling now and could feel my sister, Liz and Jane watching my every expression.

'So, Lis, I need to know – will you marry me again?'

Well, that was it. I couldn't stop the tears from falling, I was so overwhelmed. My lovely husband was going to arrange for us to get married again. Oh. My. God…John was still talking but I hardly heard the next few lines through my blubbering.

'Okay, I'm assuming you said yes. I hope you did! So, now I just want you to sit back, chill out and I'll see you soon…'

I looked at my sister and my friends who were crying and laughing at the same time. You know when you think, 'that's the sort of thing that happens to other people, not me?' Well that was exactly what I was thinking. Before I had time to wipe away the mascara running down my face and figure out how on earth my friends had kept this all a secret, I realised that we'd pulled up at the church John and I went to when we were 23 and had just got engaged. We wanted to get married there but the vicar told us we couldn't as we didn't live in the parish. At that time, we were a bit disappointed but knew we would get married anywhere – it didn't matter as long as we were married.

'What are we doing here, Lor?' I whispered to my sister. I was still in shock at knowing John had got me out of the pub to ask me to marry him – but why the car journey and where were my other friends?

'Lisa, look…' Lor pointed to the front of the church. There was Aimee. 'Oh blimey. It's Aimee. And my dad!' I sobbed.

If I hadn't been sitting down, I would've collapsed. My dad was meant to be in Spain. I couldn't speak. I was so overcome with emotion and the reality of what John had meant in the video, finally hit me. The one thing I had always wanted wasn't just to renew our vows – what I'd always wanted was to have my dad walk me down the aisle. Even though I had loved our first wedding in the Dominican Republic – two young people in love and happy to just be getting married – as the years had gone by, I often wished I'd had that special moment with my dad that so many other, lucky women have had.

John had done it. Forget the diamonds, forget the holidays and handbags. This was The Thing I had always wanted and my gorgeous husband had made it happen.

Walking down the aisle with my dad and looking around seeing all of those who had been invited to my party, smiling at me from the pews, was something I'll never forget. Nat King Cole's *Mona Lisa* boomed out around the church – it was the song my dad used to sing to me as a little girl. Talk about an emotional wreck – I'd cried buckets but now all I felt was ecstatic happiness. As my son said this morning 'It could be the best day of your life.' I guess he'd known something that I hadn't.

BLUE MASQUERADE

by T C Bridgeman

The afternoon sun slouches across the table at Café Le Procope. It sets the delicate porcelain cups a-glow. So bright, that I am obliged to shield my dirty blue eyes.

Her words not mine; from another time, another table. Now I wait in reverie for our next encounter. Each one adding to a house of cards, balanced precariously, one upon the other.

—

Walking between shadows beside the glittering Seine, I heard first about her father's death. So young, so strong, so utterly departed. Left in limbo, a purgatory of motherly distress, she emerges half-winged and breathless. The pain of always missing. To be replaced by money, comfort, the fur-lined embrace of many lovers.

She shrugs and tells me of a dream. A cool river, green banks. Alone. She is swimming on her back, arm over arm, borne along by the current.

'It takes trust,' I say.

She smiles and talks of ripples reflected in the clouds above her. Every day it is the same.

'And what if you strike into something?' I ask.

'Or someone,' she says, blushing in circles.

I match her blush for blush. It seems we are at play beneath the surface. A breeze rises in the quay-side trees.

Seeking refuge from the intimacy, I take up the mantle of adventurer. I spin tales of volcanoes spewing forth in Sicily, of masquerades in villages south of Rome.

'When I converse in Italian,' I tell her, 'I am not so Anglo-Saxon.'

In the midst of this exchange, she leans forward, into my Southern self, and asks, 'Do you know your eyes are dirty blue?'

I falter, the colour draining from my tale. I am left at the dark edge of Mardi Gras.

She cares. It cuts through the performance.

But this is all too brief. She withdraws again, her observation made. And I, conscious of the lava rising, attempt to exorcise its heat in narratives of ritual masks and winter-burning flames.

And what follows is a pattern of many stolen moments. Words, just words, in galleries and parks, among the crowd at salon soirées, at the discretion of complicit hosts. Then, as the months pass, I start to hear of wedding plans, her feelings for Him, the One, waxing and waning with every turn inside her shell. I am uncertain how to respond, shifting between sad neutrality and a plea to break free. But ultimately, I do not engage, I am content, hunting my own chimaera.

One day, her young maid arrives somewhat breathless at my door. She smooths down her smock and, with eyes cast low, proffers a folded message. Then, with a grin, she turns to flee.

It is swiftly scrawled. Her mistress suggests a meeting. A table just out of town, a Taverne rendezvous.

We are settled on a terrace above a frothing mill-stream, the ancient wheel still turning but much in need of care. She is distracted, an edge to every sharp response.

'Is there really balm in Gilead?' she asks.

My answer is another tale. So, I begin.

'There was a village once, where forest fires wreaked nature's vengeance, leaving many dead and children orphaned. The priest, a godly man with a pagan heart, builds for them a dragon. Belching fire from the brazier within its belly, it rolls through the streets, so fierce, so proud, it makes the young ones run and hide. But the priest herds them back into the village square and before their wounded eyes, lights up that dragon.

The flames reach higher than the Church roof. And the children dance as the beast burns. Till nothing is left but smouldering ash and broken spars. Then, out of the smoke, out of the vestry, comes the Green Man priest, clad in patches of gold and crimson, carrying a bough of fresh growth. And this bright phoenix leads the children home that night, refreshed and healed in spirit.'

As I bring this story to an end, I look at her directly for the first time and I see the stiff mask melt and slip away. The long face is now warm and supple. A face her father might have seen, but more than that. She is entirely open. Her eyes alive. I am drawn to look at her mouth. I have not seen the bow in it before. It was always thin, a closed purse. I put my hand out. She opens hers. I feel a ring's hard curve. A lion etched. A gift from her future spouse? But there is no recoil. We laugh in love with wickedness. The dragon is on the streets and the world is upside down. She fingers the ring, a glance to me, she slips it off. A simple sleight of hand. The charade is over. The blood is risen.

Next day, outside my shuttered window, a magpie chatters in the dawn. I have slept in a draught and wake goose-pimpled and fearful. Not for the transgression, the forbidden fruit, but because I have entered a Carnival world, no longer held in coffee cups and conversation. I am the alchemist gone one step beyond the conflagration learned in books. I struggle to contain it all.

She stirs and I am once again the smiling one. But I will not sing like the magpie. I would give myself away too soon. Does she see the anxious cleft tightening in my forehead? She makes no sign of it. Hers is a pale morning's quiet. She nestles into me with a trust that cuts deep. I am there holding her and running fingers across her body. I am ready to play but, as the dragon stirs again, the blood is sluggish and all of me is not present.

We rise as companions, naked sharers in a secret. But with clothes, our lesser selves return and defend their territory. She is uncertain. I am the joker. Her mask creeps back, sealing the breach.

That night, the maid returns with another message. A problem.

The ring is lost.

My only memory is of its smooth departure at the table. Since then no sign. I search the rooms, the bed, the guilty linen. My fear tightening all the time, as I reply:

Nothing to be found. Perhaps the magpie… I scratch out the reference. No time for drollery.

Discreet enquiries at the Taverne yield nothing.

Her maid is back. What does she know? Everything, no doubt. I swear she looks at my eyes, to verify the dirty blue. I blink to put her off. I smile. Ha! Small triumph.

The message: Will deal with the situation. A story concocted, convincing.

No doubt smoothed with strokes and gentle defiance.

Next day. The maid again. This time with fear in her manner:

Anger stalks. Though you are not the target. The Taverne bears the brunt. He would hang them all. Beware.

An anxious pause. Some weeks pass. Another message. The maid is smiling now. Subterfuge suits her.

Madame … requests the pleasure. Le Procope. 4pm.

The dragon rises in me.

—

And so, I wait, with dirty blue eyes half-shuttered in the sunlight. The bells of St-Germain-des-Prés ring out the hour. The wife of the proprietor, known to me, tut-tuts to herself, convinced there is always something amiss. I smile. She sneers. I sneer back in jest. She looks affronted but the English are always so uncouth.

Then I see them, together, in unison. They are stepping out of the carriage. I flush. Heart in head. Exposed somehow, the lover alone, but still 'in flagrante delicto'. They laugh, eyes only for each other. He is stronger, firmer, more alive than I had thought. They are the lovers.

I stand to greet them. He is all hale and heartily well met. She, restrained but confident, assured. We gather in around the table. Coffees are ordered, placed with knowing looks between us.

'I hope you don't mind me accompanying you,' says he. 'I know you two enjoy your tête à têtes.'

I am all smiles. It is a show. But do they both see my mouth drop, as her hand curls around the delicate white cup? A ray of sunshine lights up a golden ring, with lion head.

'Oh yes!' she says. 'The ring. So silly of me, really. I cannot have looked quite hard enough.'

I am silent.

Oblivious to any discomfort, he admits that he's relieved.

'I have always liked that Taverne,' he says.

It is spoken like a man who has the measure of his world. Not fantastical or whimsical. Straight down the line. So distant from my own path, which wanders, circuitous, with places to pause, to investigate what lies beneath the stone. When I regain my voice a few seconds later, I am once again in flow, the subject is Masquerade and there is another tale to tell.

UNTITLED

by Colles Breatic

S dragged her feet heavily up the stairs. She couldn't remember a time when she had despised herself more. Guilt blended beautifully with the terror tingling on her skin. Just the recipe for a void that could swallow one whole if left to yawn wide open.

'Wake up.' Reluctantly, she shook her daughter gently. 'Wake up, I need your help.'

Avery found it almost impossible to comply with her mama's plea. It was 11.30pm, a time of deep slumber for any normal girl of eight, and she was dazed.

'What's wrong mama?'

'I need you to pray with me.'

'I said my prayers before going to sleep.'

'Avery, there's a man coming whom I don't want in our home. I shouldn't have said yes, he's about to arrive and I'm scared! I don't know what else to do.'

That night she would learn two things for certain. Number one, her mama welcomed unknown men into their home to make ends meet, and number two, prayer works.

Unable and unwilling to wait for her child's response, S peeled back the covers and grabbed her little girl's hand. She led her silently out of her small, safe bedroom in the direction of the family living room. The smell of their evening meal lingered. Avery shivered missing the warmth of her bed, wondering dozily if her little brother was going to be in there too or had he been left to sleep? He wasn't there and Avery wished she had been left to sleep too.

'Santa Maria, madre de Dios...' As she pulled her daughter down to join her on her knees feverish whispered prayer spilled from S's mouth. They were touching foreheads, as if God might hear them better from their makeshift temple.

Hearing her mama's sweaty tone roused Avery from sleep completely, nailing her to that room and that moment and nowhere else. Words of supplication soaked the silence while undulations from the cheap polyester carpet dug deeper into Avery's sleepy knees. Who was the man that was coming? Why was he coming? Was he going to hurt them? Avery became infected by the panic her mama had been carrying alone up until that moment.

She chimed in with her own earnest supplications. The child was too young and too tired to comprehend the implications of that moment, but her mama's desperate actions had already set to work laying waste to Avery's burgeoning youth.

X YEARS LATER

'It's not all sex, sex, sex Avery. Most of the men just want someone to talk to. They're lonely.'

'I don't want to hear it mama. I thought you'd stopped all this!'

'It's regulars only now, I stopped taking new clients years ago. They come, we have a cup of tea, we chat. Sometimes a cuddle, and they leave.' S tried to explain the inexplicable.

'I can't believe that you're still doing this...at your age!' With arms folded, Avery faced her mama square-on framed by the doorway of her childhood bedroom. She was fully aware of the contempt dripping from her eyes. And fully conscious that she did not want to stop it hoping to hell that it hid the crushing disbelief and betrayal that was prickling her body from head to toe. Neither luck nor hard work had been friend to Avery, and she was back home penniless at thirty-four. She was adjusting to many things.

'Avery, you can't just turn up here and expect my life to stop. Either you go out or stay quietly in your room until he leaves. He'll be here any minute!'

The night the hard carpet had dug into her soft knees crawled back into her mind. She'd prayed like she had never prayed before that night and it had worked! That man never showed up. She and her mama had sat stone-still in the moonlight, dreading the ring of the doorbell. But he never came! Avery wondered where God was now as she shut the door on her mama without saying another word.

The doorbell rang. With an ear on her door Avery heard the friendly muffled tones of an unknown man being ushered into the intimacy of the master bedroom.

#Mr

CHAPTER 1
THE RABBIT HOLE

by Angela Buckell

'Breathe Natalie, just breathe.' I had my eyes closed tight, I could hear the words, the command, I just couldn't do it, something was on my chest pushing down really hard, it felt like a vice being turned which was stopping me from breathing, at the same time the tears were pouring out of my eyes.

'Natalie calm down, it will be alright,' the words were firmer this time. I could feel her stroking my hair, her breath on my face as she whispered in my ear.

'Please, Natalie we love you, please stop crying.'

Crying, she thinks I'm just crying. It's so much more than that, doesn't she know, can't she see I'm dying? I can't do this anymore, I can't cope, I can't handle the rejection.

'We will get you help, we will find someone to help you cope, don't let them do this to you Natalie, don't let him, you're worth so much more.'

It's just lies, she's just saying that. If that was true why am I here again, feeling like this? Why do they treat me like this, It's too much. I just want to be left alone, I'm worth nothing to anyone, I can't find my way out this time, I just want to stay in this blackness, this darkness where I don't have to think about anything, think about nobody, face nothing.

'Oh Natalie.' She's holding me now, tightly, I can feel her heart beating against mine.

'Please, it will be alright, I promise you.' I could hear the desperation in her voice.

I can feel her tears, wet but warm on my face, she makes me feel safe, but she can't fix this, no one can. If I open my eyes I will see her cry as well as feel her tears, I open my eyes anyway and look at my Mum. She's on her knees by the side of my bed holding me like a baby as I just lay there, but then I guess I am still her baby. I'll never have children no one will ever love me enough to want children with me.

'We will get help' I hear her say, it's like she's convincing herself.

She's looking at me. It's like now I've opened my eyes she thinks I'll be OK, she has no idea. Why does she love me? I hate myself so why doesn't she hate me? I hate everything about me, I feel worthless, ashamed that I let myself be treated so badly, she must be so disappointed in me. She has an ugly, fat, horrible daughter who no one wants. I wouldn't want me as a daughter if I was her.

'Natalie, it's not you, it's them, they just can't handle someone so lovely and kind like you, they just want someone to mess around with.' How many times have I heard her say this?

If only that was true, if that was the case then why as soon as they end things with me they get a girlfriend, start a relationship and find happiness? Why do they deserve that and not me? And there's that pain, that feeling, I feel sick, every time I think about it, I start to cry again I just can't stop. It's like something has switched on inside me that I can't switch off. The darkness around me is back, closing in on me, squeezing what life and love I have left out of me, leaving me feeling empty inside. I close my eyes, I feel like I'm falling down a hole, like Alice down the rabbit hole. If only I could, fall to another land, another world, where there wasn't this pain, this feeling of numbness, of being unwanted. I can hear her voice again, but this time it sounds like it's coming from above me, from the top of the hole, words slowly tumbling down, letter by letter.

'You're beautiful Natalie.'

'You're kind and full of love.'

'Anyone would be lucky to have you.'

'Don't let them win.'

'Don't let them bring you down.'

'They aren't crying at home.'

'They don't care.'

So many words, too much for my head, they're spinning round and round, I curl up in a ball, don't they call that the fetal position? I can feel a cover being put on top of me.

I'll make you a cuppa, and then I'll run you a bath.'

I must have stopped crying at some time if she's talking about making me some tea. I hear her stand up, open my bedroom door and walk down the stairs.

I open my eyes, they feel swollen and sore from crying, my room is in darkness. I'm still curled up my legs tight to my chest. I cuddle my large teddy, Romeo, who is sitting on my pillow behind my head. I pull Romeo close to me, I start crying again, I wish I could stop, I wish I could feel normal again. My mind won't switch off, what is wrong with me? I just don't understand anymore. Why can't I see guys for what they are? I don't want to go on, I don't want to live. The pain hurts so much, I can hear her walking up the stairs, she tries so hard to make it OK, to tell me the things I need to hear, I normally bounce back. I just don't have the energy anymore, the fight's gone out of me.

'Shall I switch the light on?' she asks.

I can see her silhouette standing at the door. I close my eyes again, make it go away Mum, I wish inside my head, I don't answer her.

'I'll just leave the door open a bit so you get some light from the hallway,' she walks into my room.

'I'll put your tea on the side, and run a bath for you,' she goes to walk to the bathroom.

I scream at her 'Tea won't help,' and straight away regret it. I know it's hard for her as well. She comes back in my room.

'I know it won't Natalie, I wish it was as easy as that. I'll run the bath anyway.' She doesn't shout back she just replies in a quiet sad way, which just makes me feel more guilty.

I slowly sit up, twist my legs round and put them on the floor. I stand, I feel weird, my legs feel heavy with every step I take. It feels like I can't support myself, everything is an effort.

'Bath's ready.'

I look up to the bedroom door, Mum's standing there, I slowly walk towards her, my shoulders drooped. I'm dragging my feet, she puts her arm around my shoulders as she guides me to the bathroom. She's undressing me, which is just as well as I don't think I could manage to do even that. I put one foot in the bath to first test the water, I feel the wetness surround my foot, the water feels warm and inviting, I lift my leg and put the other foot in holding onto the sides, I sit in the bath. The warmth of the water comforts me, she starts to wash my back, the warm water falling down my chest I have an overwhelming sense of sadness and hopelessness like nothing's ever going to be right again, I start to cry.

'I know it feels like the end of the world Natalie, but it's not, he wasn't the right one for you.'

Just words of comfort again, I'm not sure if they are for me or her.

'I just want to lay in the bath for a while,' I look at her as I speak.

'OK,' I know she's unsure, she gets up, 'I'll just leave the door open a bit in case you need me, you can call.'

'OK,' I reply.

As soon as she's gone I lay down in the bath, the warm water covers my body like a cocoon. I close my eyes and put my head under the water, I'm back at the bottom of the hole, but this time it's warmer. It's still as dark, it's so quiet, not a sound yet the quietness is somehow deafening. I open my mouth and scream but there's no sound coming out, I scream again and again, still no sound. Please someone hear me, help me! All of a sudden I can't breathe. I sit up quickly, I'm back in the bathroom, in the bath I'm gasping for air, my breaths are short and sharp, then my breathing starts to regulate again. I stand up, get out of the bath and put the towel around me, I slowly sit down on the floor I think of him and start to cry.

I can hear her in the kitchen putting the kettle on. I just lay there, my eyes still sore from last night, I don't really remember much after my bath it all seems so surreal. I remember my Mum finding me on the bathroom floor, my head on my knees and me just sobbing, then climbing into my bed with Mum putting the covers round me, whispering comforting words. I must have fallen asleep, a restless sleep. I had dreams of me falling down that hole again but this time there was no bottom, as I was falling I was passing my Mum, my Dad, Alison my best friend, I tried to grab them, but I couldn't reach, I was falling too fast. My long hair was blown upwards with the speed I was falling, I felt scared, I knew I had to reach someone before I fell to the bottom, if there was a bottom or was I falling into emptiness, darkness into nothing?

I can hear her talking to my dad, I wonder what she's saying? I know I need to get up but it's so warm in bed, plus I know as soon as I get up I have to face everything. I put my cover over my head, it feels like I'm in my own world, no-one can come in, if they can't come in they can't hurt me, I feel so alone.

'Natalie I've made you some tea' I hear my mum's voice, its close so I know she's standing next to my bed

'Ok I'll come down' I reply from under my cover

I hear her walk out, I push the cover off me, a shot of cold air hits me, I pull the cover back over me again I know I can't stay in bed all day even though it's Sunday and I have no work. I need to get up, push through this thick, black, unrelenting fog, through this heavy weight I can feel pushing me down. I think of him, and a shooting pain goes through me. My heart feels like it's broken into a thousand pieces. I know I'll never let anyone in again, I know I've changed I can feel it, I can feel all the self-doubt, the self-loathing, I can't believe this is happening to me. Where have I gone? Where's the person I once was, happy, confident, positive? I'm trying to think back to that time, before I entered into the world of lies, deception, fuckboys. Was I to blame? Did I expect too much? Just because I was honest and didn't play games, was it fair to think everyone was like me? Did I want too much too soon? Did I seem too clingy? My head starts to hurt I can't do this right now, I close my eyes and hope sleep offers some comfort.

It doesn't, I toss and turn I just can't seem to get back to sleep, yet I am so tired,

'Natalie are you up?' my Mum yells from downstairs.

'Yeah' I yelled back, but I'm not, I'm still in bed, I slowly pull my legs round and put my feet on the carpet, I stand up, stretch and walk towards the bathroom.

'I'm having a shower' I call down to my Mum.

In the bathroom I look in the mirror, my eyes look terrible, all red, swollen and dry, not that it matters anymore what I look like, who cares? I don't. I undress and step in the shower. It's lovely and hot and just for a minute I forget everything and everyone as the hot water covers my body, it feels so comforting.

'Natalie, are you alright?' There's banging on the bathroom door, it's my Mum, I love her dearly but I wish she would just give me some space.

'I'm fine' I yell above the noise of the shower.

I quickly wash my hair and body, I turn the hot shower off and straight away I'm cold, I step out of the shower and put the big bath sheet around me. It doesn't take me long to get dried. I walk to my bedroom, I dress automatically, just into leggings, jumper and trainers. My hair is still wet, but I'm lucky it goes into loose curls when I leave it to dry by itself, so I just leave it. I don't want to stay here, I just need to be on my own, I need space, I need time. I run downstairs

'Mum I'm going out, I'll text you' I call as I rush out the door.

'Bleep, Bleep' I know before I even read the text on my phone that it's from my Mum, I keep walking, it's fresh out but windy. The wind stings my face especially around my sore eyes.

People pass me as I walk by, I don't really notice them and they don't notice me, I turn into the High Street, it's busy even though it's not a big High Street, some Take-aways, Nail Bars, Coffee shop and a big food shop and of course a Café.

I look up, it looks like rain. I pass the Café, then I stop and walk back. I look through the window, it's quite busy but the sky is turning dark, rain's coming. I make the decision and go in, I push open the door. A few people turn to look then turn away and carry on their conversations. I pick a juice from the fridge, pay and sit down at one of the tables.

As I sit there, I put my head in my hands, all around me I can hear the clacking of cutlery as it's being put in the dish washer, the till tray opening and closing, babies crying, chairs scraping on the floor as people pulled them out to sit on, then push them out to leave.

I look around, so many people around me, yet I have never felt so alone, I overhear the conversation on the table next to me

'Really she said that?'

'Yes I know I couldn't believe it'

People are on their phones texting not really listening to the person they are with, while others in a rush shovelling down their food as if every second eating is a second too long. Life, it just goes on, no one knows how anyone feels, just faceless people to each other. I wonder what would happen if I stood up and yelled 'STOP!' like really yelled, at the top of my voice, would everyone stop? Then like in slow motion, forks would be hanging in mid-air, the contents falling, the person's mouth open ready to receive it.

Is anyone looking at me, thinking, is she ok sitting there all alone? But then is anyone really ok?

I'm so tired, feels like I haven't slept in months. My eyes are sore and my eyelids keep closing, I rub them as if somehow that will keep them open.

I twist the lid on my raspberry and blackcurrant drink, I take a sip, well more of a gulp really, it's still cold. I look across the café and see an old lady sitting at a table, looking around and I wonder what her story is?

She looks like her mind is a thousand miles away. Is that what I look like to someone looking in?

I can smell an orange, yes someone is definitely peeling an orange, the smell is so strong it just seems to fill the air. I yawn I just want to sleep, will my life ever be the same again? I know before I think it, it won't.

I can feel my eyes closing, my head getting heavy as it falls on my chin. Wake up! I tell myself, I need to get up and go for a walk, for some fresh air. Now it's the noise of my chair being scraped back as I stand up and walk towards the door.

I can hear the rain as it hits the pavement outside, it sounds like small marbles hitting the ground, lots of them all at once. It's hammering against the windows of the café, like it knows how much I'm crying inside, as I watch the rain falling I have this urge to run outside and be part of it, the wetness, darkness. My hand reaches out to the door handle, it feels cold, I push it down, open the door and step into the rain.

You can smell it, when it rains, the freshness in the sky. The sky looks stormy, it's now a heavy downpour, I'm just standing still as the cold, icy rain lands on me, my hair, my face, my clothes, within seconds I'm soaked, wet through, but I don't care. I tip my head back and face the rain head on. CRASH! Thunder, you know it can't hurt you but it still makes you jump.

'You ok?' I turn round sharply and then I see her.

Unlike me she wasn't soaking wet, she was standing under an umbrella smiling at me as if it was normal to see someone standing in the rain, drenched through.

MOONLAND

by Otilia Galca

'The sensibility of my today is like a shadow wandering around, haunting the carriages of the train.'

Iggy sniffs Petra's palm and puts his head on her knee. The dog seems to always know when she needs reassurance and his touch softens and relaxes her at once.

'Iggy...' she says to herself.

Petra turns her attention to the couple sitting opposite from her... she thinks that they are fresh in everything that is life. She imagines the man whispering in the woman's ear:

'Who loves you back?

Who is more romantic than you are?

Who turns to you at nights when everything is changing? Who waits with you for that last midnight train?

Who sits in silence and lets you listen to the rain?'

Petra is thinking that tomorrow the sun would be new and likewise, things beneath. Her thoughts seem to be leaking from her insight and staining her clothes that now smell of fear combined with excitement.

Outside, the moon has framed the earth, its lost lover from before times. One can almost hear the music of the stars, the bohemian poetry of writers; if one listens.

As Petra types in the code to her flat, she comes back from inside her heart. So warm and safe, at last. The cosy living room smells of geranium from the obsessive display of candles. There are pots of lavender, peace lilly and aloe vera throughout the house and the same tendency for floor lamps throwing a yellow light that seems to melt and leak onto the wooden floors, giving them a waxy look. Petra is so happy in her flat.

It is still early... not time for dinner yet... The creatures will come out in a few hours and so much work will have to be done.

Petra walks out into the tiny garden. The autumn air smells like Mother Earth's skin. She imagines that's what it would smell like if nature embraced her whole body into a long hibernation. The garden is also full of candles, beautifully hand-painted flowerpots and plates; there are several rustic wooden chairs and a charming table that seem impeccably clean, in spite of the falling leaves and autumn wind. The table sits in the very middle of this small garden, it has an indecisive shape; pretty much like that garden. This whole space looks like it has been broken from the moon and fell on earth, gluing itself to the little corner flat occupied by Petra, in the very middle of Kensington. And that's exactly how it happened!

Petra is 27 and she has been working as a probation officer in Kensington and Chelsea for a few good months now. She is tall and slender, with a long brown hair, fair skin and beautiful hands. Her brown eyes are not a wow factor of her demeanour, however, when Petra gets emotional, they seem to hold all the rain drops that have ever dropped on earth. She has left behind her family and friends and has chosen to not know anyone, apart from the people she must tolerate at work. It's not that she does not love people, because she does with all her heart. Closeness though can ruin the result of her mission.

As she walks to the kitchen to start dinner she thinks of the lab.

'Iggy, you must be hungry!'

'Alexa, turn TV on. Thank you.'

'Good evening!' The familiar News lady's voice breaks the silence.

'There may be life on the moon. A spacecraft that crashed landed on the lunar surface had spilled tiny bugs across it. What's more, the new residents are tardigrades – considered the most resilient life form on earth, they could be able to survive on the alien surface of the moon?

The visitors made their way to the moon on board the Beresheet probe, which was designed to become the first private lander to successfully arrive on the surface. When it arrived in April, however, it crashed, and the mission was aborted. For most people and the majority of the mission, that catastrophic event brought everything to a close. But the tardigrades – true to their reputation for being hardy – might have survived the crash and been spread across the surface, where they could be living on today.'

Petra serves Iggy his food. The black lab wiggles his tail in absolute content and gives her loads of kisses that land on her hands and forearms before sticking one to her forehead too. He then starts wolfing down his dinner.

The woman and the dog are having dinner in the beautiful light floating in the house from the countless floor lamps; Petra is watching the news and the dog is contently watching her. A whole world has come into place in this tiny flat; a world of which you will be thinking and remembering at times. That is the wish and dream of every storyteller.

***

And breathe in 1, 2, 3, 4 and out 4, 3, 2, 1

Breathe in 1, 2, 3, 4, 5 and out 5, 4, 3, 2, 1

Breathe in 1, 2, 3, 4, 5, 6 and out 6, 5, 4, 3, 2, 1

Petra is lying on her back, feet up on the creamy wall, meditating. She is in the darkest corner of her flat for mediation; one needs darkness to fully crave the light.

The clack sound penetrates breath 4 as it went in and exploded inside Petra's stomach.

Although she has been expecting it, the fall and the clack still startle her.

Petra goes back to her breathing and allows her mind to accept. She only moves when both her mind and body are in a sync of peace and acceptance of what it is to come. She slowly lifts her head off the fluffy rug that bears amazing patterns of flowers, birds and bees forever motionless in a picture of harmony meant to make one yearn.

Petra moves towards the opened door to her garden and Iggy calmly sniffs her palm as if to reassure her and remind her that he was in this with her.

There it is: red; almost burning red. The stone has fallen right in the middle of the table that holds it like the precious gem that it is. Amber shapes are moving and travelling across the diameter of the stone. It is in full cycle and it looks like a powerful one.

Petra gently touches it... without fear, just with respect. The door to the moon is once again open ... through the shadows of the night, the sound of an old music breaks the silence of the garden and hundreds of souls and thoughts embrace Petra so tightly. The creatures show themselves one by one; they first show wide open beautiful eyes and with slow movements they come closer and closer, until they all surround the woman holding the precious stone. Petra can't help but think of the tartigrades and what are they up to on the land of dreams.

***

'I wonder if the clouds know when we watch them. They seem in such a rush... so mysterious.' As Jacob thinks this, he also thinks that is so out of ordinary for him. He is in a state that makes him question the weed he smoked the night before.

Time is stationed in this heavy morning air that smells like a way too ripe banana; half pealed and half rotten. September is heading towards another end. His birthday is approaching like this recurrent nightmare that however hard he tried to block, it only turns stronger.

The tiny kitchen smells of bacon, coffee and eggs. Food is probably one of the few things that make Jacob content. His belly is showing it. Another day when he will have to try and swerve living like a decent man; another day of lying, deceiving, pretending. The man sighs heavily as he sits on his tired sofa and starts eating his breakfast whilst watching the morning news.

There is no choice! He has to take each day as Chapter 1 until, perhaps that moment comes when he is ready for The End. What keeps the ending away, he doesn't know. Nothing gives him joy apart from awfully unhealthy food and getting high... and gambling. It is that simple. He feels too ashamed to pray. Talking to God! Jacob rolls his eyes and walks to the window to light his first joint of the day. Yeah, he will definitely be needing this in order to face the outside world. He wonders again, what would be the colour of the thought to put an end to all this absurdity. Life is like a wall made of heavy stones which you have to carry, polish and arrange methodically. His wall will never stand.

Mornings are initially so blurry; almost as if the clouds descend at night to rest over his body. His mind still feels under a cloudy influence, almost as if to give him strength to get going... deceiving him that it is all right.

He gets himself going; he showers and dresses. He styles his thick and curly hair and gives himself a really good look in the mirror.

'At least I am handsome,' he thinks.

Jacob has strong masculine features, thick brown eyebrows, long eyelashes and his brown beard surrounds his lips protectively. He is definitely not fit... far from. The thought somehow always makes him smile. As he looks at his reflection in the dirty mirror, he thinks that it is like he is made of four different characters: one represented by his face, one by his body, one by his mind and then there is that one that he could not get in touch with: his soul. He knows he has one but it must be hiding somewhere deep where all of his self-destructive behaviour could not reach. Jacob feels scared thinking that his soul is slowly rotting, leaving the other three behind.

At his front door, his breath stops. There is a letter addressed to him from his solicitor. Jacob wipes the sweat off his forehead before he opens the envelope. He reads through the almost three pages, without thinking or feeling. There's nothing new; just a reminder that at his first court appearance, the magistrate asked to see a pre-sentence report and that he is going to be contacted by a probationary officer to set a date. Jacob goes back to his bedroom and folds the letter neatly. He then puts it in his bedside drawer which is completely empty.

As he walks out of his house in Acton, heading to the train station, Jacob feels restless and scared. The sun has entirely defeated the shadows of the last night and the wind is blowing quietly through the trees. Jacob thinks about his soul for the second time this morning. His soul is the last memory of God within him... It is still there and that scares him and at the same time gives him courage. He is experiencing a completely new feeling... one that he has heard of, but never experienced. Jacob feels hopeful! Divinity has not abandoned him... not only that, it has actually been sitting somewhere inside him, waiting to be seen.

The train arrives and Jacob suddenly realises that there are only a few people on the platform. He cannot recognise any of the faces that he is used to seeing every morning, Monday to Saturday on the platform. He gets on the train looking at his phone to check the weather. It is going to be sunny and warm. Close to 24C. Jacob looks away from his phone. Why is everything so weird this morning? It almost feels like he is on the wrong train and that it is going the wrong way. Fewer people too! Why on earth are they so silent and staring as if they know each other and have agreed to meet on this train?

Suddenly something that feels like an earthquake stops time. Jacob's vision blurs and he closes his eyes in panic and there it is: he remembers the dream that he had the night before: he had woken up to a world where the moon had disappeared.

Jacob opens his eyes and everything is back to normal. He wipes the sweat off his forehead and realises he has dropped his phone, when a schoolgirl hands it to him. 'Are you ok, Sir?'

'Yes, thank you. Thank you!' He smiles nervously and thinks that he must be going crazy. He is getting off at the next station. Really? He has been on this train for 20 minutes? Something is definitely wrong with him. Maybe the drugs and lack of proper sleep are finally getting at him.

***

When Jacob's present time is disturbed on the train, the creatures would have been reading and writing in Petra's attic for over ten hours. The sound of typing has been thundering and although it is literally a beautiful sunny day, a morning rain of words is pouring and cleansing Jacob's stream of thoughts from distance. The space in Petra's attic is timeless while the creatures are connecting to the stone that carries messages from the Moon Tree. While hosting the readers and the writers of the moonstone, time is allowed to escape from the attic and wander in worlds that only exist in nightmares.

The work is still ongoing, lining the words on the path that lead to the creation of a new hero. The creatures are only short and look like strange foxes that have adapted to some kind of human form. Never have they actually explained to Petra how, but she suspects that they have evolved in decades of living amongst people and that the moon has chosen them to be the contact with humans because they are close enough and yet invisible. Petra herself has been saved by the grace of their intervention and then stayed loyal to them and to the moonstones.

This morning, Petra's soul seems to struggle in recognising the face looking in the mirror. The light outside is quiet and then it gets loudly bright as the Sun beams from behind the clouds. She swallows bits of the bright light and sunny emotions start galloping towards her heart. Sometimes, melancholia becomes an illness of her surroundings and that is when she should return to her medication but no. No! They have taken her away from the creatures and the moonstone before and she won't let it happen again. Who could treat that brutality then? This is all she wants and cares for.

Petra drinks her coffee and then prepares Iggy for his morning walk. She feels a persistent pressure in her chest and growing tall towards her head. 'Patience,' she thinks. 'Patience makes time glossy. Patience is the art of seeing and surpassing time. Patience is an art that I am still learning to master.'

She puts Iggy on a lead and walks out into the morning air. The city is streaming secrets stolen from the night dreamers. Petra is thinking of the poem in the writing; a poem about a cycle that starts with autumn and ends with its singular sun; it is a poem about two planets. This world is too much of a rotten dream that needs saving from an endless symphony that lacks harmony. This world to her is insanity.

'No!' She screams in her head.

'I will not go back to medication. I do not need to be in this world. The moon is my mother now.'

The rest of the walk is a blur; a mix between breathing exercises, tears, hysteria and hope. Iggy stops a few times to sniff her palm and bring her back.

As they walk back in the flat, one of the creatures greets them with enthusiasm and what seems fear.

'This is the morning! You must call him at once! We don't have much time before he loses faith. Many forces are working to save him. Not enough people though and that is what he needs. The Writers have been affecting his perception already and that can lead to dangerous reactions.'

Petra looks at Lina; her red shiny coat and wide open beautiful eyes... her nails are painted pink and she never wears human clothes, unlike some of the others.

'OK Lina! I will call him now.'

Petra picks up her mobile phone and dials the number she has saved on the day of the court hearing.

'Mr Jacob Cristophi? Good morning! It's your probation officer calling. I wondered if you could come and have a chat this week. What times are best for you Monday to Friday?'

Petra listens and scribbles something in her notebook.

'That is absolutely fine. Shall we say Wednesday at 1pm? I will email you the address and confirmation of our meeting. That is all you will need. OK, great! I will see you then, Mr Cristophi.'

Petra puts the phone down and looks at Lina. Her eyes are bright and the brown turns into a ruby, just like the stone that now streams in the blood of Pany, one of the Readers. 'Wednesday.'

Lina looks overwhelmed.

'The moon is the hostess of all madness, the mistress of all darkness and tomorrow will rain...'

'What happens when it rains?' Petra asks fearfully.

'The rain holds the past. It will mean disaster.'

They are both standing in the sunny flat and looking towards the red table. It has the shine of rubies and gives them strength.

THE OBITUARY

by Victoria Hassett

Part I – Ursula's story

Chapter One
In Bed

I lay in bed with a mug of freshly brewed Earl Grey served with a twist of lemon, just the way I like it. My Irish terrier, Mikey, snuggled by my side, his small, warm, body resting reassuringly against my legs. Outside the spring rain pattered against the sash window on this sleepy, slow, Saturday morning. This was my sanctuary and I was in no hurry to leave it. Sighing contentedly, I reached for the newspaper.

Alice, my nineteen-year-old daughter, had tried in vain to get me to read the online newspapers, but it really wasn't for me, I preferred a crisp news-sheet and the honest smell of printer's ink. It was one of the very few small pleasures in my busy life and worth savouring. Besides, I always read my paper from the back first, not the sport, but amongst the small ads, film listings and births, marriages and deaths. All the flotsam and jetsam of people's lives is there, if you know where to look. It wasn't nearly as satisfying to devour the paper in such a way on an electronic device. I hunted for my reading glasses lost somewhere in the folds of my white duvet when my iPhone rang.

'Hi Mummy.'

'Hello darling.'

Mikey jumped off the bed, making me spill my tea. I cursed under my breath.

'Have you got Mikey on your bed? You know daddy would never allow…'

'If you recall Alice, 'Daddy' decided to run off with his vacuous secretary and therefore has no right to have an opinion on what goes on between me and my Egyptian cotton,' I exclaimed.

'She wasn't his secretary; she was his PA.' Alice replied.

God. I could do without this. 'Well, whatever she was darling, she took her job description far too seriously. Alice, did you ring for a reason or was it just to remind me of my single status?' Fuck. Why was I being so facetious and to my only child too.

'Well, no. Actually mum, I was wondering if you are going to be home tonight. I would really like to see you.'

Alarm bells started to ring. Alice never willingly came home from Uni. Maybe she'd run out of money again, or was ill, or possibly, God forbid, in some sort of trouble. However, now was not the moment to confront her on this. Experience had taught me not to challenge my daughter head on. No doubt she would explain later.

'Of course, darling, I'm always here, be lovely to see you. Text me when you're on your way, we can chat later.'

I forced myself back to the small ads and the lonely-hearts columns; there was no point worrying about Alice now.

I had toyed with the idea of signing up to 'Soulmates', the Guardian's online dating site, but it just didn't feel right. I'm much too 'old school' for that, so the lonely-hearts columns it would have to be. Not that I'd actually replied to any – it was too soon for that – but there was no harm in looking. Now, here's one I thought, 'Suave and sophisticated looking for a fun-loving, mature woman to pamper.' Hmmmm, I could do with some pampering. Fat chance of that happening any time soon, I muttered as my phone rang loudly at me again. I looked at the screen expecting it to be Alice again. But it wasn't.

'Hello, Simon,' I answered wearily.

'Darling you. How are you? Well, I trust?'

'Fine Simon, what's the problem?'

'Ursula sweetheart, I've been up all night worrying about the play. We open in just under two weeks and the last scene is still a disaster, not you though sweetie, you're always fab.'

'Thanks,' I mumbled insincerely.

'So, I've been thinking, can you make it to rehearsal a teeny bit earlier than 2pm today? There's so much to go through I don't think my nerves can cope with it all.'

His voice took on its usual wheedling tone when he wanted someone to do him a very big favour.

'What time, Simon?' I sighed, resigned to his request.

'Darling you're a star! Shall we say 11 sharp? I'll bring coffee and pastries. Ciao Bella'.

Damn. My Saturday was quickly being hi-jacked by other people's needs. I was determined to stay put, at least for just another precious five minutes. I turned the page and read

Ursula Jane Saunders
1966-2017

Bloody hell! That was me – my name, my year of my birth, I didn't know I was dead though. I grabbed the paper again and read on:

Ms Ursula Saunders, daughter, of the late Professor Daniel Saunders and Mrs Kate Saunders, died unexpectedly last night. Ms Saunders was highly respected in her chosen field of play therapy and had been instrumental in setting up the degree course at Brunel University where she had worked for the last 20 years of her life. She pioneered many new and revolutionary techniques such as filial play therapy and had been a consultant to Lambeth social services. She was a champion for the abused child and volunteered her own time working in local schools training staff to be able to identify children at risk.

In her spare time Ms Saunders enjoyed performing in amateur productions at The Minstrels Playhouse based in West London.

She leaves behind her an only child, Alice McKenzie.

Funeral to be arranged. Family flowers only.

I felt numb. This was my life. Still is, the last time I checked. What on earth.. a million questions flew through my head as I tried to comprehend. My phone rang again making me jump. I tentatively looked at the screen, wondering what next? With relief I saw it was only my friend, Cathy.

'Hi Ursula, are you up, or still festering in bed?'

I laughed, a high pitched almost hysterical laugh – possibly with relief that I was still alive. 'Hi Cathy, I'm still in bed.'

'Good. Look, Ursula, don't be angry with me, but I've done a really silly thing and I feel I need to warn you about it before hand.'

I was finding it difficult to follow what she was saying. My brain was still trying to process the notice in the paper. Was it her that had written the obituary as some sort of crazy joke? But Cathy wasn't that nasty or even that imaginative enough to pull off such a henious prank. And why would she anyway?

'I know we're best friends Ursula and have been forever, so please don't hate me.'

Ok, so what the hell was coming next?

'But I've invited David and his new wife to my party tonight.' She paused, but I didn't respond. She carried on, 'Ursula? I hope you don't mind but Brian felt I really should invite him. After all we have known each other for a very long time.'

I was still having trouble taking in her words, 50th? David? Tonight? And then the penny dropped, God, she was talking about her birthday party.

'Oh,' was all I could think of as a suitable response, and 'I see.' She'd actually invited my bloody ex. 'That's fine, Cathy,' my voice betraying my words, 'It is your party after all.'

'Hey are you OK? You don't sound yourself, I expected at least one 'Fucking Hell!, Cathy.'

Should I tell her about the obituary or the fact that I had forgotten all about her party and had just arranged for Alice to stay instead?

'God Cathy, you won't believe this but…'

As I told her everything that had happened that morning, including Alice's unplanned visit, I tried to laugh the whole thing off as some silly mistake. Maybe some rookie at the newspaper had got overexcited and published the wrong obituary, maybe another university lecturer had popped their clogs last night, somebody with a similar sounding name and they had pulled up the wrong person's life story by accident.

Cathy was not so sure. 'Darling that's awful, who would do such a sick and nasty thing? Are you OK? Do you need me to come over? Only I've got the caterers arriving shortly and the marquee is about to go up in the garden.'

I could hear in her voice that she was willing me to say I'd be alright.
'I'll be fine. Promise. See you later'.
'Ok darling, if you're sure. Invite Alice to come along tonight too, it would be lovely to see her.'
'I'll see what mood she's in, Cathy, you know what she can be like.' I replied, knowing full well that the last thing Alice would want to do is hang out with a load of fifty-somethings.

I closed my eyes for a moment to try and compose myself. The rain seemed quite menacing now as it pounded against the windowpane. Mikey had disappeared somewhere leaving me feeling suddenly very alone. I shivered. I needed to get a move on if I was going to make it to rehearsals by 11 o'clock. I'd just have to push this disturbing incident to the back of my mind. There was no time now to find out why this had happened and who was behind it.

Forcing myself to move, I rolled out of bed. Placing both feet firmly on the floor, I took a deep breath to steady myself and for some ridiculous reason promptly burst into tears.

Chapter Two
Rehearsals

An hour later I'd arrived at the rehearsal studio. As usual, Mikey was with me. I decided to take him for a short walk first, mainly to try and clear my head more than for his sake. We took our normal route around the block; past the town park and the children's rec where Alice used to play as a young child. Mikey seemed to be enjoying the familiar smells and several times he stopped in his tracks to peruse an enticing odour. The rain had left the pavements shiny and fresh and momentarily the sun peeked out from behind the darkening clouds managing to slightly lift my flagging spirits.
I gave myself a little pep talk. Come on old girl, it's only some stupid mistake, it's not like anyone wants you dead or anything sinister like that, there's probably a rational explanation. I resolved to ring the editorial department first thing on Monday morning to find out who had written the obituary and under whose authority. But, for now, I had more pressing needs, such as how I was going to cope with my ex-husband

and his new wife at Cathy's party and why my daughter was making an unscheduled visit home. But first there was Simon and his on-going neurosis about the play to attend to. I quickened my pace and manoeuvred my way through the heavy double doors marked 'Theatre Entrance'.

'Ms Saunders how are we today?' A cheery voice greeted my arrival.

'Hello George, to be truthful I've felt in better spirits.'

He looked concerned. George, our dependable caretaker, always on site and always willing to lend a hand whatever the request might be. He had been at the theatre for as long as anyone could remember and had a lovely old-fashioned gentlemanly air about him. One of his quirks was to address everyone by their title and surname. I'd given up long ago trying to get him to call me Ursula.

'Well I'm very sorry to hear that Ms Saunders, let me know if there's anything I can do to help.'

'Thanks George, I will.' I smiled at him and noticed for the first time how blue and sincere his eyes were. He held my gaze for a moment longer than I felt comfortable with and I turned away blushing slightly. I changed the subject.

'Has Simon arrived yet?'

'Yes, he's through there now with the set designer running through a few changes to the scenery.'

Oh, dear God, I thought, what now? 'OK George, if you get a moment later on do you think you could take Mikey out for a little walk for me? I rather think this is going to be a long session.' I didn't wait for his reply knowing that he would say yes and pushed my way through the studio doors. Simon was in mid flow.

'For God sake Ursula, save me from amateurs!'

'Simon, darling, we're all amateurs here, otherwise this theatre would be in the West End instead of the back streets of Ealing, at least we all try our very best!' I could see that Simon was angling to start a 'bitch fest' about somebody and quite frankly I didn't have the patience for his histrionics today.

'Shall we start Simon? I haven't got all day to spend rehearsing, don't forget it's Cathy's 50th tonight and I've got to make myself look gorgeous, which, these days, takes far longer than I have the time, or indeed, the energy for.' I slumped down on a hard-plastic chair after my rhetoric.

'Oh yes, the beautiful Cathy. What time is kick off I always forget the small print.'

'It's 8pm Simon as well you know. I'll pick you up at 8.30. I'll book the taxi.'

Simon pulled a face at me. 'I'm not sure I can afford the time Ursula darling, there's so much to get through before opening night.'

'Don't be silly Simon, there's free champagne and besides David and his floozy have also been invited and there is no way on earth you are going to abandon me to spend the whole evening on my own trying to avoid eye contact with them both.'

'OK, as it's you, and as there will be champagne I will come, but don't expect me to be civil to that Ex of yours, in fact it would give me great pleasure to tip a glass of bubbly over his greying head.'

'Now, now, Simon watch your blood pressure and if anyone is going to tip champagne over anyone's head you can rest assured it will be me that does the tipping. Besides I'm not sure Cathy would appreciate us starting a fight at the party of the century do you?' We both sniggered at the thought.

Simon turned to greet the rest of the cast as they started to trickle in. I saw George through the door window looking over and I raised my hand to him and pointed towards Mikey as a reminder to take him out later. He waved in return nodding his assent and I turned back to Simon who was in full flow about the scene changes.

***

The day wore on and I was beginning to feel my eyelids grow heavy with the weight of too much inactivity and boredom. I'd had enough. I gestured to Simon that I needed to go and make a call and went outside. I checked my phone, one missed call from a number I didn't recognise, probably another call about PPI, and one text from Alice letting me know that she was on her way. I suddenly remembered George taking Mikey out of the studio over an hour ago, his office door was slightly ajar, and I went to push my way in without knocking, I stopped on the brink of the doorway as I heard George talking to someone.

'Oh, yes, you're a lovely boy, aren't you? I bet you get lots of lovely cuddles from your mistress, don't you? I bet you even get to sleep with her, you lucky fella?'

Was he talking to Mikey? I decided to knock after all. George immediately sidled out, with Mikey by his side.

'I was just bringing him back to you Ms Saunders, he's had a nice long walk and he's been sleeping like a baby ever since.'

'Oh, that's lovely. Thanks ever so much George.' I turned to Mikey and tickled him behind his ears. 'What a lucky dog you are to be treated so kindly by George.' Straightening up again I spoke directly to George.

'I don't know what I'd do without you.' I flashed him one of my sparkling and, hopefully, winning smiles. The sort of smile that, in the old days was reserved for flirting with men but was sadly very under used nowadays. I could see the effect it was having on dear George, as this time it was his turn to go red.

'Well I'd better be making a move, I'm off to a party tonight and need to get my act together if I'm going to look drop dead gorgeous.' Now why had I said that?

'You always look gorgeous,' he mumbled not able to give me eye contact any longer and I suddenly felt mean for teasing him. Half an hour later I was about to leave when my phone rang. It was Cathy.

'Are you OK, Ursula? I've been worrying about you all day.'

'I'm fine, Cathy thanks, been at rehearsals for most of the day, just making my way home now and I'm in a bit of a rush actually.'

'OK, but there is something I've been meaning to talk to you about, something personal.' She sounded subdued and not her usual bubbly self but before I could respond she continued, 'never mind darling it can wait until later.' Her tone made me think it might not be good news.

'If you're sure, Cathy,' I sighed. 'Be sure to tell me later.'

PERFECT HARMONY

by Glenn Mackenzie

It was a beautiful summer's afternoon. Michael strolled along the country lane, his lungs drowning in the sweet smells of nature with every breath. Arriving home from school he put the key in the door. He loved being home. This moment gave him a feeling of contentment and relief. He felt protected from the outside world. A universe rich in beauty but shadowed by a simmering broth full of threats, sadness and danger, ready and waiting to feed each newborn day.

His ritual on arrival from school was a sequence of events carried out with military precision. Door locked and checked. Shoes taken off and placed next to the lovely wicker chair. Tie off, folded lovingly and placed gently over the chair. Walk through to the kitchen, take a large bowl, pour cereal, pour milk, take the spoon with the fine matt finish handle and then switch on the TV and sit in his favourite seat next to the window. The view was always mesmerising in its beauty and changed each day as if newly painted for his arrival. The luscious greens caressed his eyes and quenched his senses with a numbing calmness. He had arrived. How wonderful it was to devour the splendour of far reaching hills running for miles and darting through the thick clouds like a forest wind. How fortunate he was to enjoy this avalanche of colours and imagery of nature.

Michael stared at the spectacle through the window whilst stirring the silver spoon in the clear bowl. It was actually a small cooking bowl allowing a larger portion of Sugar Puffs, his favourite. The mixture slowly turning a golden brown when stirred, allowing the wheat to bleed its sweetness and gorge itself on the fresh milk. He relished this moment.

It was difficult to pinpoint exactly when it all began. It crept up on him absolutely unannounced like an intruder, a stranger, standing there, looking over him and telling him what to do. It was irritating and unsettling. At times it could even case nausea. If not calmed and put to rest it would leave a sickening sensation of lingering anxiety and guilt. One's actions and thoughts could cause awful outcomes and harm to the individuals involved. The desire to make things right and do the correct thing was overpowering.

He didn't think anything of it earlier. 'It was a thought.' 'It'll pass,' he thought, trying to convince himself it would disappear within the vast web of streets and alleyways of his imagination. 'Oh please,' he muttered through gritted teeth. At this moment his delicious cocktail of peace and tranquility had vanished. It was a small measure of anxiety but enough to poison the moment and create unrest. The stunning view from the window had now become blurred. His moment soiled by an intruder. The irritation began to slowly run through his blood picking up speed with every beat of his heart. 'Oh please, leave me alone. Please just leave me alone,' he whispered to himself. 'What is wrong with you Michael,' he uttered. 'Why should they be harmed or even die? What does it have to do with me? I don't need to be involved? Why me?' he thought. He sat anxiously, mid spoonful, trying to reason with himself. Again he whispered, 'What is wrong with me?' With his mind racing nervously he knew that this time it was not going to go away. That thought was lodged deep inside his head.

His diagnosis was conclusive – he was sure. This one had to be laid to rest. A disturbing feeling like a priest never allowing him to repent from his thoughts and a court condemning him to an eternity of life imprisonment with his mind as a cellmate! His soul wanted justice but his mind wouldn't grant it! 'Why did I have to do this? Why?' he mumbled. He knew it was wrong but his conscience plagued and mauled him. He knew he couldn't concentrate until this deed was done. Oh how he despised this feeling. This ritual. This torture that slowly crept up behind him like a deadly plague. It entered the body and drowned the mind. He needed to take action otherwise it would torment him. It would ruin his evening. It needed to be fed. It needed to be calmed. It was the only solution. A mental battle throwing him to the ground in bloody defeat on every occasion. It was a powerful force. Oh my goodness – it was powerful!

It was his secret after all and a dark one at that! Of course he knew that. Every day of his life he was reminded of it. A secret nobody could ever have imagined. He thought about it many times. He analysed and studied it. He knew he had to step back and admit the truth. He had been given an incredible talent. His thoughts became actual real events. His mind possessed full control over the final outcome of the person in the thought whether good or bad. His actions controlled their destiny. He never asked for it. It was frightening but he owned it whether he liked it or not.

It was getting dark. He never liked the darkness, and it made him feel vulnerable and open to threat. He was going to have to go outside again. He needed to free his guilt and cleanse his mind. It had to be done. He had no choice in the matter.

Michael loved music. He would listen to records in his bedroom for hours, lost to the world. He fell in love with the cello. Any form of cello music he found absolutely beautiful. He would practice for hours. When listening to a record he would listen to part of a composition over and over lifting the stylus back and forth over the vinyl to repeat the part. Again and again, each time absorbing the beauty of the phrase. Sometimes he did this for hours at a time. Whilst practicing the cello, if a section of music proved difficult then he would develop an exercise for that specific part and repeat it over and over until perfect. He found something overwhelmingly pleasing about playing the same note slowly over and over, each time listening to the differences in sound. It could be the angle of the bow. It could be the pressure of the bow against the string. There were so many variables and each made a miniscule difference in sound.

His earliest memory of things being somewhat 'different' were when, at the age of 12, he remembered unplugging the record player from the wall socket every evening before retiring to bed. It had to be unplugged. After all, something could happen during the night and cause an electrical fault, which, in turn, could start a fire. He couldn't possibly go to bed allowing that thought. He recollects that on occasions whilst pulling out the plug he would think of something very strange indeed. A thought would just enter his head, uninvited and unwanted, resulting in a feeling of dissatisfaction and guilt. The thought, almost always, was distressful and disturbing. It was a strange feeling and very difficult to describe. Imagine singing Happy Birthday and suddenly the song stops! No name! Nothing! The song does not reach its final destination. In musical terminology this could be described as a 'Half Cadence'. A melodic or chord progression that needs harmonic or melodic closure. A sensation of being incomplete or suspended. It isn't allowed to come to a natural close. Imagine a distressing thought that is left lingering and screaming for closure and only you can repeat the action that provoked the thought and this time cleanse it to something pleasing allowing closure. That's what it feels like. The action wasn't completed satisfactorily because it ended with an intrusive thought.

In the majority of instances the intrusive thought involved an illness, a death or a fatal accident. The only way to resolve this was to repeat the action coinciding with the thought and cleanse the thought with a much nicer thought. The nice thought allowed for complete closure in the mind and most importantly eliminated any distressing outcome. It was the name being sung in Happy Birthday. It gave final closure. A 'Perfect Authentic Cadence'. Michael was responsible for the closure or not. He controlled the destiny of the person at stake. So after various attempts he would eventually reach a satisfactory resolution in his mind but this may require pulling out and pushing in the plug maybe four, five or even six times for example. All depended on his thoughts at the time. If he wasn't happy with the intrusive thought then the process had to be repeated until a stage of thought satisfaction had been achieved. This would allow a relaxing night's sleep.

Michael had turned 19 years of age. He was practicing the cello in his room on this day and had the radio playing gently in the background. Years had gone by and he had become an expert on his 'ways' and had accepted that he was rather 'different' from others. Yes, he would have to leave the house and walk to the bridge he had crossed on the way home earlier and cross it once again to rid the thought that had been left. Now he was content. Geraldine would no longer be involved in a fatal car crash as the moment had been cleansed and the horrible thought was now redundant. He had managed to repeat the process but this time arriving at a satisfactory conclusion. It wasn't always straightforward though. Sometimes it didn't work on the first attempt. As for getting dressed, well that was the worst and very difficult to manage. The mornings were the worst. They could be quite tiring. He remembers one day taking off and putting on his shirt at least twelve times. This was a very timely process and it could start at underwear and carry on through socks, shirt, trousers, etc. Stairs were problematic and also leaving places that you knew you would probably never visit again – that was quite exhausting. The thought of leaving a nasty thought that couldn't ever be cleansed was extremely difficult. Pavements were another issue, especially the cracks. Michael became a master at disguising his mannerisms and walking patterns and the people he walked with would be none the wiser. He was a professional at returning to look at something in a shop window just to cleanse the awful thought that he had just left there whilst passing.

It was a Friday afternoon and Michael was practicing a Prelude by Bach on the cello. He loved J S Bach. It was the Cello Suite No. 1 in G Major, BWV 1007 to be precise. It required great technical ability and hours of practice and repetition. Of course, it goes without saying that Michael had become a master of repetition! This qualification was incredibly useful in the process of learning a musical instrument and unknown to him at the time would also prove to play a crucial role in developing his future career and success.

He paused to allow his hands to rest and his attention turned to the interview playing on the radio. It was a medical programme where people called in to discuss their problems and issues. On this day a woman called Sophia had called in. She sounded mid 30s, very well spoken and was asked to explain her problem and why she had called in. She was timid and her hesitation and nervousness was noticeable. She sounded embarrassed. With helpful prompting from the radio host she admitted that her problem was getting dressed as she puts her clothes on and off if she doesn't feel right about the way she had put them on. She thinks strange things and has to do it again. Michael stared into the void opposite in utter disbelief. A strange feeling came over him and he sat up in shock. He carefully laid the cello against the wall and sat there digesting this incredible revelation. He had a strange feeling inside as if someone had just delivered some awful news. It was disturbing to hear someone describe this routine, his routine. It was as if someone had just walked into the room and stolen his intimacy, his secret. They had stripped him naked and exposed him to the world. He was completely stunned by this confession. He continued to listen with intense concentration, absolutely fixated by what Sophia had to say. It was a very strange feeling indeed. The woman could easily have been describing him. It was very unsettling. He didn't know what to do. When did I ever feel like this he thought? He knew he had felt it before, then suddenly it hit him. The blood panicked and rushed from his head causing a feeling of faintness. He remembered!

On going to bed one evening he carried out his usual wall plug ritual but on this particular day it was difficult. Exactly how many times the plug was pulled, put back, pulled out, put back, again and again until he was happy couldn't be remembered. His bedroom was directly next to his parents and on getting into bed he heard his father utter the words, 'once is enough you know, you just need to do it once'. That terrible feeling of being found out, being caught in the act. It was a sickly feeling. On this occasion it was a real intrusion. Someone had really entered one's private world completely uninvited. The embarrassment. The matter was never discussed with his father ever again.

Sat there hoping that the interview would never end Michael savoured every word pouring from the radio. He sat stunned listening to the voices, symptoms, discussions and explanations. The guest doctor in a very softly spoken voice eventually reached the moment everyone was waiting for. Michael moved closer to the radio breathing slower and listening with intense concentration. What was wrong with her? Why did she do these things? What was it?

He felt an enormous feeling of relief. Something lifted from his being leaving a rush of adrenalin speeding through his veins. He had travelled through life carrying awkward baggage. It was strange and extremely annoying but he accepted it and admitted that something was different about him. The human mind adapts to its surroundings very cleverly even when, deep down, one knows there is an issue. A gigantic cloud had been lifted. The excess baggage had dropped and hit the floor with an almighty bang. An intoxicating moment that allowed him to breathe freely and admit that it wasn't madness after all. Like seeing another human being after years of solitude and realizing that you are actually not alone. There were other people who lived the same life as he did. He reached for his cello and started playing the prelude from the beginning. His concentration drifted from the music and he whispered slowly, emphasizing each word – 'Obsessive Compulsive Disorder, O-C-D, Obsessive Compulsive Disorder, O-C-D,' etc. He continued playing and then suddenly stopped, placed the cello against the wall, reached over and turned the radio off and on and then off again.

Still sat in his favourite chair Michael could see it was getting even darker outside. His beautiful view had vanished into the night. He stood up, turned off the television and placed the bowl on the kitchen table. He put on his light bomber jacket and stepped out the front door once again. He locked the door behind him then tried the door handle twice.

'Back to the bridge again,' he whispered.

DESTINY: A MEMOIR

by Carol Martin-Sperry

Chapter One:
Lightning Strikes

I first saw him on a ski-slope in Italy in April 1966. He was tall and lean, extremely good-looking with finely chiselled features, soft blue eyes, sensitive, classy. He wore a navy ski suit and a pale blue sweater. From snippets of what I could hear he was French.

I watched him ski away, he was so graceful. Although I was instantly attracted to him I didn't feel I could follow him. I felt wistful because I did not actually know who he was. Would I see him again? He was elusive.

The spring snow was soft and giving, the slopes wide and forgiving, the sun shone in a crisp blue sky, chasing away the dark gloom of winter. The conditions were perfect. When the sun is shining and the sky is dazzling and the snow creaks beneath your skis there is nothing like it. Focus on following your skis and you are present in the now, no past no future, no room in your mind for stressful thoughts or feelings, your mind is wiped clean. Exhilaration, freedom, floating and flying, yet connected to the earth and the sky against the panorama of the strong and sometimes violent beauty of the mountains, it is one of life's peak experiences right up there with falling in love, good sex, the perfect meal, the beauty of nature, the sun, the moon, the stars. How lucky I was to have experienced them all at once.

At the end of every afternoon we would stop at a busy bar/café at the foot of the slopes for a hot drink. The jukebox played the Isley Brothers *Twist and Shout* and the Beatles sang *She Was Just Seventeen.* It was always crowded and smoky, the windows all steamed up. The atmosphere was jolly as we all relaxed after a hard day's skiing and swapped stories about our endeavours on the slopes.

Once I saw the beautiful boy there and again I felt a vague but curious longing, like sensing the delicate scent of summer flowers and herbs. It wasn't desire exactly, it was more complex, there was an aura about him, I felt dreamy.

I just did not have it in me to approach a total stranger and casually introduce myself. Casual did not feel right because there was something special about him. I spent the rest of the trip hoping to bump into him, longing wistfully for him to notice me but I did not see him again. Destiny had knocked on my door but I hadn't heard it.

The 60s had erupted three years earlier when I was 18. I threw out my ugly pointy padded bras, the nasty girdles and stockings. I cut ten inches off my skirts and dresses. I had my hair cut short and straight by Twiggy's hairdresser, goodbye to horrid curlers, hairdryers and back-combing. What a relief! This was liberation from the restricted and repressive dull 50s and I fully embraced the spirit of the time.

The Beatles were breaking and Paul McCartney was living with his girlfriend, the actress Jane Asher, who was a friend of mine. Visiting the Asher house was challenging. A gaggle of little groupie girls were camped out on the doorstep. There was a secret code for ringing the doorbell which changed regularly. We were special because we were allowed in. Paul had a small room at the top of the house where he wrote his songs, often with his toothbrush tapping on a glass to keep the rhythm. He knew I was fluent in French and he asked me if the words in *Michelle* were correct (they were). Another time we were all sitting round the kitchen table when Paul came in and said, 'I've written this song called *Drive My Car*. Should I put 'Beep beep mm beep beep yeah!' in it?'

Of course we all said yes. What a privilege!

Canada

In the summer breaks I would visit my father who lived in Toronto. In July 1964 I flew to Montreal for the first time. My boyfriend Andrew and his diplomat father met me at the foot of the plane with a car and whisked me through immigration and customs in front of everyone. So grand! I felt very special.

In town I got myself noticed with my miniskirts and dresses, usually worn with no bra London-style. Once I literally stopped the traffic on a main road, everyone staring at me. I was surprised but not at all self-conscious, proud of myself. Later in Toronto at the exclusive country club we belonged to, my French bikinis attracted the same kind of attention. There was talk of banning me, or at least my bikinis, but I remained defiant, a sophisticated European in that stuffy town.

In January 1965 I moved into a 4th floor walk-up mansion flat off Kensington High Street which I shared with a changing cast of flatmates over eight years. It was action central, non-stop parties and sleepovers, French, Canadians, Americans as well as friends from Cambridge. London was absolutely the place to be and I was at the centre of it, a true 60s chick, a mover and a shaker.

Apart from Beatles and Stones gigs, I saw all the major Motown stars, Ike and Tina Turner, Aretha Franklin, Jimi Hendrix, Cream, Led Zeppelin and many others. I saw James Brown in the Albert Hall, standing on the shoulders of a friend and dancing in the aisle. Black American artists loved London because there was no segregation, they could stay in hotels and eat in restaurants with everyone else. I also saw Bob Dylan in the Albert Hall when he went electric to the dismay of the folkies and to my joy. I went to see the Four Tops there too, Otis Redding at the 100 Club, soulful and intimate. I hung out at the Establishment club, Hades, Tramp, the Speakeasy and burgeoning discos.

I went to see Antonioni's *Blow-Up* because I was in it as an extra. My scene was in a disco where the band smashed their instruments and we danced to the music. Antonioni had wanted The Who, but they refused, so he got The Yardbirds instead.

Life was intense and exciting.

Lightning Strikes

I was in Helen's flat in Montreal for 24 hours. I had spent Christmas 1966 at my father's in Toronto and I had decided to fly home via Montreal. Andrew and I had broken up and I wanted to show him I was over him. I was curious to meet this new girlfriend. She was a successful artist and Andrew was managing her career. Not only talented but pretty with it, small with dark hair and sharp intelligent hazel eyes.

She introduced me to Philippe who was standing at the window looking out at the falling snow in the half-light of a January dusk. He certainly looked French in his navy Shetland sweater, loafers and leather jacket. He was very good-looking. I held out my hand.

'Bonsoir, Philippe.' He smiled at me politely.

'Bonsoir.' We chatted in French.

'I have just been skiing in Vermont,' he said.

'Oh, I love skiing!'

'So where have you skied?'

'Davos, Zurs, Megeve, Verbier, Cervinia…'

'Ah, I was an instructor in Cervinia last year.'

I look at him.

Lightning strikes.

The world stands still.

The hairs stand up on the back of my neck

A shiver goes right through me.

The earth tilts beneath my feet.

It's him.

I am in love for the rest of my life.

'It's you!' I say in stunned awe.

'Me?' He holds my gaze.

'Yes, you. I saw you there.'

And I described his outfit, the crowd around him, the café on the slopes. He gave me a warm smile, he was intrigued, there was a connection.

I'm English, he's French, I saw him in Italy and I met him in Canada. An astonishing coincidence.

He was and is my destiny, the love of my life.

The four of us went out to dinner to an intimate French restaurant in the smart part of Montreal. I was sitting opposite Philippe, bathed in his aura, hot and flushed. I was finding it hard to talk.

'So why are you in Montreal?' I asked him eventually as we studied the menu.

'My father got me a job here with a French import company. He wants me to go into business but it's not going to happen. And you?'

'My father lives in Toronto. I'm here because I spent Christmas with him. Andrew is my ex, I was curious to meet his new girlfriend. I am flying back to London tomorrow.'

'And how come you speak such good French?'

I was flattered.

'I was educated at the Lycée Francais de Londres and I did a French degree at university.'

He smiled at me, his soft blue eyes looking into mine. My heart thumped.

We went on to a club and danced to *A Whiter Shade of Pale*, slow and close. I breathed into his neck as he pressed his hand on the small of my back.

When we left he helped me with my long Russian princess coat with its glamourous fox fur collar and cuffs. I could feel his firm hands on my shoulders, I was shivering but not from the cold.

He took me back to Helen's flat. She was staying at Andrew's, the flat was ours. We necked on the sofa in the dark. I was floating in a daze, tremulous, expectant. The silence was heavy with promise.

Then he asked me if he could spend the night with me, 'dormir' (go to sleep), not 'coucher' (have sex). I said yes, but just to sleep. He showed me care and respect, I trusted him. We went to sleep in the big bed, naked, the Scandinavian duvet keeping us warm against the ice and snow of the Montreal winter.

But I woke in the night, that first and only night as I thought, and I turned to him and opened up to him and we made love, so easy and straightforward, so simple and uncomplicated, with his expert delicacy, such tenderness. I felt at peace lying next to him.

He left at dawn to go to work. I woke up later in a hazy daze. He called me before I caught my plane, said he'd write. Oh yes, I thought. Why would such a boy bother to write to me after a one-night stand? Yet deep in my soul I recognised that something momentous had occurred.

His letter arrived soon after I got back from Montreal. Could this be more than a one-night stand? It looked promising. I had to see him again, I knew he was my destiny. I had to make it happen. I had to be daring and bold, I had nothing to lose.

In early April I wrote to him

'I could come to visit you, if you are not too busy, but let me know quickly'.

'Viens'

The telegram said 'Viens'. 'Come'.

So I went.

I was so brave, 22 and motherless. I see myself crossing High Street Kensington to the bank in my purple Biba mini-dress with the matching suede knee-boots.

I took some of my mother's jewels out of the bank for the airfare. Even then I had the courage to make things happen, to set things up. I was on a journey, focussed and determined.

My flatmates at the time thought I was crazy crossing the Atlantic to see a boy I had known for 24 hours but I knew I was in love. I had to go, there was no choice. The sensible one said 'You're mad, you don't know anything about him.' The romantic one said 'Yes, you must go! Follow your heart!'

I remember being on the plane talking to the stranger sitting next to me.

'So why are you going to Montreal?' he asked me.

'I am going to see a boy I have known for only 24 hours,' I replied.

I told him how I had first seen him in Italy, he's French, I am English and I met him in Canada.

'Wow! That's incredible!' Yes, it was literally hard to believe.

I remember deciding that if Philippe was not at the airport to meet me, I would turn around and fly straight back to London.

I remember walking through customs at the airport with my matching Samsonite luggage towards the frosted automatic glass doors. I knew this was a defining moment in my life. The doors slid open, he was standing there smiling. I was locked into my destiny.

We drove through the city. He walked me across clumps of dirty clotted snow to the back of an Edwardian house in the Greek quarter. 'Shh!' he said as we climbed up the iron stairs on the outside of the building, 'I'm not allowed girls in my room.'

The room was in the attic. His bed was a mattress on the floor. His bedside table was an orange box. His clothes hung from a string by the shower with dry-cleaner hangers. There were candles and a record player. His books and records were piled up in a corner. This was the most romantic room I had ever seen.

He made everything seem so easy and natural, despite the fact that we hardly knew each other. We laughed about it although we both knew this was serious. He lived in the here and now, present in the moment he was in and he took me there with him, paying me full attention, making me feel I was the centre of his world, creating an unbreakable connection. How could I not love him…

We made love endlessly. I was profoundly and irrevocably in love, drowning in sex, bound to him emotionally for the rest of my life. Whatever happened to me I knew then and there that he would always be my touchstone.

He left for work every morning and naked I would burrow down deep in the bed, holding his tartan woollen scarf to my face because it was both rough and soft and it smelled of him. I drifted in a drowsy heightened haze, high on post-orgasmic hormones. He came home in his lunch breaks. We made love. In the afternoons I walked through the city. We didn't know each other but I did know that he was kind, generous, open-minded, serious. He treated me with respect.

One morning the landlady came up to the room with a stranger. I was still in bed and I could not reach my clothes. I pulled the sheet up and tried to hide my obvious nakedness. She stiffly introduced him as her architect, her prudish Quebecois Catholic disapproval burning me. I had blown it, Philippe would be given notice to leave.

Back in London I held tight until the end of June, missing him, missing him. The flame burnt steadily, nothing could extinguish it, not even my insecurity, my fear of rejection and abandonment.

Aretha Franklin sang about her soul being in the lost and found, until he came along to claim it. Yes.

The Summer of Love

I flew back into Montreal in the summer of 1967, *Sergeant Pepper's Lonely Hearts Club Band* under my arm, as yet unreleased in North America, but received with rave reviews in the UK. Big stuff.

I was back on an intense high with him. He told me of his plan to pick up a car in New York and deliver it to San Francisco, the ultimate road trip. I was so excited! We would drive across America together, to San Francisco where the counterculture was blossoming, free love was everywhere and the hippies were wearing flowers in their hair.

But later he told me, 'You are too much in love with me, Carol. I am not going to drive across America with you, it will end badly.'

In my heart I instinctively felt he was right, I knew how insecure I was, but I was devastated.

'I am not going to marry you because our lives are too different, we don't share the same goals. You are too much in love with me. I don't love in that way. I am very independent and you are too dependent on me, I can't take on that responsibility. I am also quite selfish and fickle.'

He was so grown-up, gently spelling it out to me, still tender and affectionate. I could not speak, I was in shock. I just nodded and looked away.

'But whatever happens I will always be there for you, you can count on me. For now I just want us to feel good together'. As my tears fell he said, 'It's not the end of the world Carol, you were not made to be unhappy.'

He was so straightforward and honest. I felt very small, there was nothing I could say. But still I trusted him and believed him because I loved him.

Meanwhile nothing had changed. We made love all the time, whispered to each other, listened to sad songs, slept in each other's arms.

DEAR ANNA

by Dia N

Dear Anna,

I hope you never read this letter. I wish I didn't have to write it in the first place. But this is probably the only way I can deal with my feelings without hurting anyone. To be honest I am quite tired of my feelings, they seem like such a burden. So sensitive and so ready to be offended.

I started writing to you on a number of occasions but was left staring at a blank screen. For someone never short of words, it has been a struggle to express myself.

It has taken me a while to understand why I felt the way I did... angry, fearful and confused. I was mirroring your mental state. But instead of being next to you, helping you overcome these intense emotions, I sat across you and projected them back. Though, to be fair, I did come to you with empathy but soon retreated, internalising your hurt as mine. Your arrival was supposed to be about you. Sadly, it became about me and my helplessness.

How do you keep loving someone who resists you every moment, at every level? I still don't know the answer to that. You try all you can with the expectation that something might work. On good days you prop up hope, dreaming of a time when everything will be alright. On bad days you crumble and lie still, watching a little bit of yourself die. A lot of me died in those early years but no matter how I felt, I now know you felt worse.

I wish I could change your past. You should have never experienced what you did. I could not protect you then and if the few years we have had together are any indication I may not be able to again in the future. Your fight for survival began at 20 days. We don't know if you experienced a gentle touch or felt loved in that time before we met you. Irrespective, it had a huge impact on your personality.

You were eleven months old when you joined our family. It was one of the happiest days of our lives! That evening we saw a beautiful journey ahead of us. It had the promise of all things good! It was also the beginning of something we had not anticipated. By then you had developed a set of behaviours that had been crucial to your well-being in the impersonal environment of a government home, where you needed to cry to get attention, to be fed and diapered. But you were now with your family and the rhythm of life was gentler. You didn't need to be hostile or suspicious of our every move but of course you didn't know better.

With your large curious eyes, you took in your new surroundings. The sight of a spoon moving towards you caused panic. As did entering a lift. Over time you made your peace with cutlery and even overcame your fear of closed spaces. What did not change, however, was your mistrust of people, especially me. I will admit, I was overly sensitive too. I read meaning into things I should have ignored. I didn't know where I stood in our relationship. Perhaps you didn't either. Insecurity makes one behave in desperate ways. You wanted me and you didn't, both at the same moment. You would cry to be held but when I came close, you would push me away in anger. It was a situation designed for failure. 'What do you want?' I would ask, sobbing frustratedly. You would bawl some more in response. And so it went for a while.

Your dad and brother were not immune to this either. I saw them unravel at their own pace. Your brother, just two and a half years older, who welcomed you with open arms, slowly went from being a calm and happy child to a raging mess. You didn't warm up to him and he didn't take the rejection too well. Your dad, stoic and unruffled in the most stressful situations, went into a dark space trying to deal with his own feelings of inadequacy. There we were, a beautiful family of four, wounded and suffering, unable to offer comfort to one another.

Once at an airport I saw a father carry a little girl in his arms while the mother tried to put a cardigan on her. I watched with surprise as the toddler remained cheerful. I felt a deep pang of sadness. A simple moment like this was not available to us. It took me back to the time when I unzipped your jacket in a museum to prevent you from overheating and you screamed for what seemed like eternity till we finally exited and you fell asleep drained. I wanted so much to be able to hold you and care for you but you were not ready. My heart ached for the loss of your childhood and our experience of it.

It took us nearly 18 months to reach a place where you allowed physical contact for a few seconds without fighting back. Mealtimes were stressful, as were 'goodnights'. We didn't know what would trigger you off. Some days it would be a glass of water that had been moved, on others the curtains being drawn. The first couple of years were mostly a series of exhausting meltdowns a day. On more than one occasion I thought of ending it all. A railway track, the edge of a cliff, a blade. But taking one's own life requires a lot of courage. Years ago, a friend did and my grief for her was also mixed with admiration which I didn't dare admit to anyone.

We thought holidays would make it better, that a change of scene would lift our spirits. On the contrary, they had the opposite effect. Perhaps it was the new environment that threw you off, or having an audience watch me fail repeatedly that got to me, it didn't work for either of us. On one occasion we were separated in a hotel lawn. We were watching you but you didn't know. What started out as play became uncomfortable as the minutes went by. You realised you were all alone amongst strangers and it didn't seem to bother you. We waited impatiently, hoping to see a sign that we mattered. Twenty minutes later I couldn't take it any longer and came after you. There was something strange about your manner, you didn't seem like a two-year-old. It left me disturbed. Upon our return I narrated the incident to your doctor. She listened and said, 'she is a child who has suffered trauma and come to expect nothing.' It broke my heart! All your behaviour leading up to that moment had been an attempt to protect yourself. How had I not realised this earlier? Maybe because I was too occupied with my own feelings to think about yours. In any case this understanding helped me move the focus from my disappointment to your pain.

Was the trauma due to the multiple care givers you had had in the first year of your life or was there more to it? We will never know. What we do know is it robbed you of innocence and everything that comes with it. Childhood was a luxury you couldn't afford, you were competing with adults. Daddy and I encouraged you to enjoy your age but you were in a hurry to grow up. You were an incredibly quick learner, you could brush your teeth, use a fork and even dress yourself very early on. But this independence became a challenge in other situations when you literally put yourself in harm's way.

I often wondered if we had made the right decision for you. The effect of nutrition was easy to see and of course you had more opportunities now... but were you happy? Did we unintentionally add to your trauma by trying to integrate you into our family? It had been a wonderful, smooth ride to care for your brother, was it because he shared our DNA? Did it finally come down to that? Were we incapable of building a bond with a child we hadn't created? We didn't think so but the thought did present itself a number of times.

Then one day we received a call from the child health services. Good news, our case had been approved for counselling. We were hopeful but soon realised it was a long, slow process. Week after week for a year we travelled to the other end of town to see counsellors. Some sessions were difficult and left us exhausted. Our family dynamics had gotten worse. Your brother was unrecognisable, and Daddy and I could barely see eye to eye on any matter. Separation was a very real possibility. I have no idea what kept us together. Perhaps a happy shared past spanning two decades or perhaps the wisdom that we were all equal victims of the unkind situation. We pulled along somehow.

Just when you think things can't get any worse life throws a surprise your way. The Covid-19 lockdown began. Staying at home gave us the opportunity to bond with you but every hug and laugh we shared came at a price. You brother was hurting even more, if that was possible. He saw our growing proximity with you as a threat to him. He refused to celebrate his seventh birthday, left mean notes for us around the house and spoke incessantly to prevent anyone else from talking. Your meltdowns reduced but his grew. In his words we were the world's worst parents. What had we done!

Friends told us we were brave but we felt like imposters… clueless and ill equipped to handle the situation. This had been a crisis spanning years and we were fatigued but we told ourselves as long as we were standing, we weren't defeated. With this in mind, we navigated our lives between two traumatised children, one day at a time. The counselling continued over video calls and then they said they were ready to try intense therapy. We went from once a week to thrice. The sessions were hard to sit through, you were uncontrollable and found different ways to express your anger. We were asked to not interfere. You often drew pictures of our family excluding your brother. We watched in pain and silence.

Slowly these engagements became calmer. We started playing games and you even asked for help. It may not seem like much, but we know the effort it took to build that trust. We don't take it lightly. And then suddenly out of nowhere you and your brother started playing together. You did not stop fighting altogether but you were able to stay in the same room, exchange a few sentences without being confrontational. It has been four days since you have become 'friends' and I am filled with relief and nervous excitement. I don't know how long this will last but this is the furthest we have come. I write this as I watch you build train tracks in the backyard. You have your opinions, but you are mostly civil to each other. I must have told you a dozen times since morning how happy it makes me to see you two get along, so much so your brother has asked me to stop saying it loud as it embarrasses him. He did give me a hug after that. I take that as a good sign. It fills my heart with so much pride and emotion.

We have a lot of hurdles to face in the future. At some point you will realise you did not come from my body. And as you enter adulthood you will want to know more about your biological mother. There are a lot of missing pieces to that puzzle but we have a sense of the overall picture. Sadly, it is not one that will bring you any comfort. We will cross that bridge once we get there. For today, I am happy with what I have. As you grow older and question everything that has happened to you, I am certain you will also question our love for you. I have often worried about that but like your wise and kind doctor once told me ... love comes in different forms, not giving up is also love.

I hope you will remember we never gave up on you.

You will always be our little girl.

Love,
Mum

OUT OF THE BLUE

by Karen Pearson

Life was busy, and this was the way that Kim liked it. She had been working at London Met for seven years now and she felt that with her new role she had reached the pinnacle. She entered her office and glanced at the sign on the door 'Head of Undergraduate Programmes' and gave herself a mental pat on the back. This was not how life was supposed to have panned out, but her career had saved her all of those years ago when she had decided to stop being a doormat and make herself the centre of the story.

At school, Kim had always been a bright and eager youngster who seemed to be accomplished at whatever she chose to try. But at the age of 15 she seemed to shed her skin and became a truly troublesome teenager, intent on kicking back at authority and shunning her studious life and friends for something a little more rebellious. Needless to say, that this sent her grades crashing to the floor and she left school with her tail between her legs and dreams of going to college and university just that, a pipe dream. Her parents were always there to support her and never chastised, they would let her make her mistakes. With the hope that this once clever girl would make something of her life and not let her abilities go to waste. She hoped that they could see that this was exactly what she had achieved, albeit a little later in life than expected.

Kim often reflected in this way, it was as though she lived in a dream world where she didn't want to wake up. How had she managed it? But, today she must be on her game to deliver her first academic speech as head of programmes, her inaugural lecture, was how this had been announced. She must not let anyone see that she did not deserve this position and for any of her academic colleagues to annihilate her with clever words. She closed the office door and opened up the laptop on her desk, she refused to let the self-doubt creep in and distract her. The nagging insecurities weren't going to win today!

As usual there were quite a few emails that had landed since she had left her office the previous evening. This form of communication had been her go-to for many years now, but it meant that whenever she sent anything out there was the risk that a barrage of replies would be received, a mountain of responses would then be called for, and so the continuing increase in her mailbox size would march onwards and upwards. However, her system of organisation had been honed over time and she started to organise her inbox, with the goal that after an hour (she never liked to spend more time than this) she could deal with anything that needed an immediate response, with the knowledge that she could then 'crack-on' with running her new department. She ran most of her life in this way; compartments of time that meant tasks were started and finished. The lessons learnt in earlier life had set her up to be determined never to drop down to that level again. Her coping mechanisms were tried and tested, and the results proved their efficacy. The mailbox was looking good and then something unfamiliar caught her eye.

Anything that was sent within the university, or from a partner institution, would be from an ac.uk address but here was an email from a Yahoo mail account. Did anyone actually still have a Yahoo mail account? Blimey, this must be an email address from the ark or worse still, something dodgy asking me for money or my account details. But surely not, the systems here were pretty robust and this would not have made it into her inbox. It didn't seem to have any attachments, so no trojan horses ready to hold the university to ransom. The subject was rather vague too; 'Hey I hope you don't mind me getting in touch'. This was certainly not what Kim had expected today. Who the heck was this from and if she opened it would it then send the university systems into chaos? She could feel herself getting distracted and she really didn't need this today. She would look at it again later and moved it to her pending folder.

Out of sight and out of mind she moved on to complete her task with a mental tick in the box. Focusing on the rest of her rather important day she forgot about the odd-looking email and started to edit her PowerPoint presentation for her inaugural lecture later in the day.

After work, Kim had headed to the supermarket for dinner items. Living alone meant that food wasn't that high on the agenda and cooking for one was always a bit of a sad affair. She had learnt that batch cooking was not for her, you cook a delicious dinner to then split into small boxes for the freezer for when you couldn't be bothered to cook (you still have something healthy and nutritious). However, the normal result would be that they would sit there for six months and then be chucked out when the freezer started to groan under the weight of ice that had established. No, she had learnt that lesson after several hours of defrosting, with a hairdryer on full heat, only to have found several boxes of rather unpleasant brown dollops. No, Kim didn't operate in that way and as she only had to feed herself she chose to shop at Whole Foods Market every couple of days. It was her little luxury that she afforded herself and they did great fresh meals that could be ready to eat in minutes.

With her mind focused on dinner she perused the fridges, loaded with fresh dinners, to see what took her fancy. Then she saw something that conjured a picture in her mind of the odd email from that morning. Staring back at her was a name that she hadn't seen for quite a few years, strange to see it on a vegan sausage roll 'Chapman's Sausageless Roll'. That was it, Chapman, it started to dawn on her who had sent her the email.

When she arrived home, Kim had dumped her shopping in the kitchen and retrieved her laptop from its hiding place. She had decided some time ago that leaving things on display was an invite for burglars, living alone you could never be too careful, even though Richmond was a very nice part of the city. The laptop fired into life and then she went through the various security hoops to be able to see her university inbox replicated in front of her as she sat on the living room couch. She went into the pending folder and clicked open the email she had seen that morning. Slowly she began to read, taking in the words that seemed quite surreal to her. Her mind drifted off as she replayed the event in her head again for the umpteenth time. Each time she tried to remember exactly what had happened, but it was so long ago now, and she wasn't quite sure if she was just romanticising the scene.

Her sister had always been clear on what had happened that night, but she wasn't around to ask anymore, Kim had lost that privilege some years earlier. Kim's sister had always known what to say and her astuteness and way with words had guided Kim for so long. Kim had struggled with her personal life, or lack of it, for years but she pondered with her thoughts and decided to share her news with her best friend, Jo. She grabbed her phone, went into her favourite numbers and a picture of her childhood friend filled the phone screen.

Jo had answered after a couple of rings, it was late enough to call as Kim knew that Sophie (Jo's little girl) would be in bed and she would then have her friend's undivided attention.

'Hey Kim, it's good to hear from you, how's London treating you?' Jo always asked Kim this question, she had told her on several occasions that she selfishly hoped that she would get tired of London and head back north to be closer to her friends. Kim herself fought with this inwardly every time she had contact with her friends either virtually or physically. But she had chosen this life for a reason and right now it was playing out as she wanted.

'It's fair to say that it's pretty good and I'm getting to grips with the new role,' Kim replied, 'but I'm really calling because of something that happened a long time ago and I really want to know what you think.'

'Oh?' Jo replied.

'Yeah, I'm going to forward you an email and I want to know what you think this means,' said Kim.

'Okay, it's in the ether now and should be landing in your inbox as we speak, give me a call back when you have read it.'

Kim felt like a teenager again as she waited for her friend to call her back, nervously waiting. She knew that Jo would never judge her about her past or for that matter what she might do next. She trusted her friend and normally found it hard to express herself emotionally but with Jo she felt safe and that she would always be there for her. Jo, herself, had made some poor decisions in the past but the best thing she had done was have Sophie. Even though her relationship with Sophie's dad hadn't worked out, Sophie somehow completed Jo. Even though Kim hadn't wanted to go down the children route she could see that it had made Jo the person she was today.

Her thoughts were interrupted by her phone buzzing on the coffee table.

'So?' Kim said, 'have you read it, what do you think?'

Jo hadn't even been able to say hello, not even hi could be popped into the opening of the phone call. 'Well', said Jo, 'this really has come out of nowhere hasn't it?'.

'How are you feeling about it?'

'It arrived at work! I know my profile is on the university website and of course you can search for anything on the internet these days and come up with at least some information on anyone you want to find out about,' Kim replied.

'All very true Kim, but apart from telling me how the internet works, what do you think of the actual email?!'

Jo knew Kim all too well and could see that she was skirting around the issue, but Jo wasn't having any of that and pulled her straight back to the subject in question. After all, she had sent her the flipping email so now she needed to face it head on. No more evasiveness when it came to this matter. Kim may be excellent at her job, Jo thought, but her personal life was a fiasco.

After an hour and a half on the phone with Jo, where they dissected the email and looked at what could be written in between the lines several times, they started to think about whether there should be any response.

'Does it actually have a question that needs answering?' Kim asked Jo. 'I mean, is it just an historical account of events from so long ago or what?'

'Of course you need to reply, you can clearly see that and I think that you are just being you, pulling up the drawbridge so that you don't let anyone in. Reply and then see what plays out next.' Jo was starting to lose her patience a little now and had got to the point of telling her friend what to do rather than cajoling her idiosyncrasies. They said their goodbyes and Kim promised to visit with her as soon as she could (she always did but it didn't actually happen too often). Kim then set about composing a reply that seemed friendly but not too long and without revealing too much. Once again, she detached herself emotionally even signing off the email with 'best wishes', as though writing to an old auntie.

Kim had woken up the next day feeling like her routine had been given a good bash over the head. She had ended up not eating any dinner and felt a little ropey for skipping on food. Never mind the emotional torture she put herself through on the phone and then trying to write a ridiculous email to someone who she hadn't seen or heard from in years. Why now? She could see that it was invading her thoughts again and headed to the shower to try and wake up and clear her head. She would go to Pret for her favourite breakfast on the way into work, that would get her back in track.

Just as she did every other day, Kim headed to her office and began her morning routine of firing up her computer, logging in and waiting for the university systems to kick in and retrieve her daily email mountain. She looked at her watch, 8:34am so she should really have this all over with and get to her 10am meeting with the vice chancellor's office no problem.

Skimming through the list of senders, whilst shovelling spoons of coconut porridge into her mouth, she suddenly stopped. There it was, the same email address (seriously, who still used Yahoo?) she had already got a reply. 'Okay, so let's try and remain calm,' she told herself, she hadn't written anything too bad in her reply last night. She clicked on the email and started to read, then she grabbed her phone and pinged Jo on What's App.

Sending you another email through, what do you think I should do? x

In middle of breakfast with Sophie, give me 10 x, Jo replied.

Kim sat at her desk, playing with the spoon in her porridge, it seemed to have gone cold and lumpy now. She pushed it away, that was not going to make her feel any better this morning. Her phone screen burst into life.

OMG!!! So, are you going to be able to get here this weekend? Xx

Jo was back messaging on What's App and seemed clearly excited at the prospect of me travelling north this weekend.

Come through and stay with us, I think that would be a good idea, then even if you decide that you don't want to go you are with us and we can do something nice together.'

Kim wasn't so sure it was a good idea but a break away did seem like a lovely way to spend this weekend and it would be with Jo, and she knew Jo would keep pushing until she got the right answer. Well the answer she deemed to be correct anyway.

Kim typed; Let me check the trains and I'll let you know. I really need to push on with work right now, talk later xx

Jo replied with a big smiley face emoji, that was it and Kim knew that she was going to the north of England after work on Friday, end of story.

The week rushed by, as it always did, and Kim found herself standing in front of the departure boards at Kings Cross Station. It's funny how you get used to the hustle and bustle of the city, jumping on and off tube trains with a suitcase in rush hour. It's as though you become immune to the throng of people, each one intent on making their way across London in one direction or another to reach their various destinations. Maybe home, maybe to friends, the pub, who knows. But it all happens successfully and here Kim was at her destination waiting for the 6:20pm train through to Darlington. Jo was picking her up at the other end as usual, she wouldn't let her get a taxi or pick up a hire car. It was part of the ritual and this time it was extra comforting to know that she would be there as she got off the train. Her phone lit up, it was Jo.

Are you on your way? Xx

Checking up on her as though she was a little girl again.

Waiting for the train, seems to be on time xx, Kim replied.

She had some time to go and find a little gift for Jo and Sophie, she always took them something nice to eat or a little gift for the house. It would also distract her from her thoughts as she watched the clock tick round. She headed off to the small shopping area inside the station, looking out for something unusual that the girls could enjoy. Should she buy something for Mrs Chapman? She had always known her as that, come to think of it, she wasn't quite sure of her first name. She felt silly and somewhat irrational, she didn't even know the woman's first name and yet she was rushing to the other end of the country to see her and she might not even remember her!

As she headed back to the main concourse it was now 6pm and Kim could see that the boarding sign had started to flash next to her train. She headed to platform 6 and found her seat. In the carriage she managed to push her case in between the seats so it wouldn't get bashed by other people with big cases in the luggage racks, she had suffered that experience before. She sat back and waited for the train to finish boarding and then the announcements started over the loud speaker, telling her about refreshments and not being able to smoke (not even in the loo!), she closed her eyes and listened to her breathing. What a week she had just had, her inaugural lecture, meeting with the VC's office and, not to put too fine a point on it, now on a train heading north and who knows what might happen when she gets there.

A CAT'S STORY

by Amy Pope

I've been on the streets now for almost a year and, in that time, I have perfected how to get food. If I just stroll up to the Hoomuns, meow sweetly and curl my entire body around their legs, they're mine. One day I see one and saunter up to her. 'Meow Meow Meow,' I say, expectant of food. Instead she stops and strokes me tenderly. She turns around to the other Hoomun and I hear her say, 'Oh will you look at him. He is only a baby and he hasn't been neutered yet and he is on the streets. We can't have that.'

They disappear and I stroll over to the wall and jump up to lie in the sun. Well, there was no point hanging around there with no food in sight! The next thing I know, the Hoomun is back and this time she has what looks like a box. Oooh I love boxes! I quickly jump off the wall and stroll into it, ready to play. All of a sudden, I am no longer on the ground but high up in the air. This is strange. Where am I going? I am bobbing up and down and am unable to get out. I should be scared, but something about her soothing coos into the box reassures me. A ping sounds and we go inside another box. We seem to be moving! My ears have just popped! When is it going to stop?! After what seems like forever, a ping sounds again, and we leave the big box.

She walks a short distance, stops and puts me down onto the ground. I hear her shuffling around for something. The next thing I know, a large dark wall opens up and I see a gigantic container beyond. I realise then what is happening. I've heard stories from my fellow street cats about 'The Inside'. Tales of a never-ending supply of food, treats and toys; where there are soft places to sleep and lay, rather than the rough ground that we sleep on outside. I've heard that cats that are taken to 'The Inside' are always happy. I can't quite believe it. Have I been chosen for 'The Inside'?

I'm ushered into a huge container and there is a small open box with what looks a lot like small pieces of tree in it. I walk over to give it a deeper inspection. 'Now this is where you do your business from now on?' Hoomum says, I respond, 'Meow.' The small trees look and smell funny. I won't be going in there. 'Good,' she replies. 'You understand.'

I wander off, ignoring her and start to investigate my new home. 'The Inside' is amazing! There are climbing frames – 'Now don't go jumping up onto the cabinets, those ornaments mean a lot to us,' Hoomum says, pointing at me as I look up at the climbing frame, noticing small toys placed on each level. Hurrah! We continue the grand tour and I spot scratching posts – 'Or even think about scratching the sofa and chairs,' she continues. 'Meow.' I can't wait to have a go at those!

But what's that I can smell? I lift up my nose to the air for a big sniff. I'm not sure if I am the only cat in this giant box. I can't see one though, so perhaps I can just smell the remnants of the past.

The next morning, I wake and stretch my long limbs above my head. That was the best sleep of my life, curled up on a fluffy towel. At least I think that's what they called it as it was laid down for me. I didn't even have to worry about the other cats prowling into my territory. I think I'm going to like it here.

Hoodad has walked into the room and lets out a loud yell! 'He's only gone to the toilet on the bed!', he says, screwing his face up. Hoomum runs in and she cleans up my morning poop. She's the best! 'Maybe it's the litter,' she says to Hoodad, who still has a screwed-up face, but it's less red now. 'We'd best figure out how to solve this quick, as we can't have this every night!' and he walks away.

I am being cooed over and then put back into the box. 'Meow Meow Meow,' – I am so sorry I didn't know where to poop, and I did try to cover it with a towel. Please don't put me back onto the streets, 'Meowwwwww.'

We're back into the travelling box and descending. This is it – I had one night of happiness on 'The Inside', but I am obviously destined for a life on the streets forever. Hang on, where are we going now? We are outside but we are in a small container travelling at speed. I stop meowing and look out of the glass barrier, but we're moving so fast everything is a blur.

Three hours later…

That's it, my life is ruined! I can't believe they removed my private parts! Why would anyone do that?! Hoomum has been chatting away to the evil ones who did this to me and doesn't seem upset in the slightest. And I thought she liked me!

Back 'home' – I think that's what they call it? She is rushing around and then I hear it, the beautiful dulcet tones of the tin-opening machine. I can't jump up right now, as I'm still in a bit of pain from my trip to the vets, but I can smell the sweet aroma of fish wafting in my direction. A bowl of it is placed in front of me and a surge of renewed love for her rushes over me.

A few days later… One of my favourites things is to burrow through the tunnels (sofa throw). Hoomum tuts and is always putting the tunnel back together after I've demolished it. Which is great, because then I can just carry on with my game. Every now and then, when I'm burrowing or climbing, they call out to me – 'You Little Rascal … Terror … Monkey.' What are these words! Are they my name?

I've also discovered that there is another dark wall at the end of the hallway that they always keep closed, but often go in and out of, and shoo me away from. It looms above me. I'm sure they're hiding something in there. And I'm sure the cat-smell is stronger from here. Strange!

I hear muffled voices on the other side. 'When do you think she'll be ready?' I think Hoomum is speaking. 'Do you remember what she was like last time we tried to do this? When we looked after Oscar just for one week!? She got herself in a terrible state,' Hoodad says, sounding concerned. Who is 'she' I wonder? There's a gap at the bottom of the wall and I prise my paw under it, but I can't seem to reach very far. 'They need to meet eventually,' I hear from beyond the wall. Whatever they're hiding in there, it must be important.

Another climbing frame has arrived. Oh, how they love me! But hold on. Oh no, this one is going to be tricky to jump onto, as there appears to be something blocking me. And now, they're putting my small toys into it and shutting them away. 'Let's see him try to knock our ornaments over from inside a glass cabinet shall we!' Hoomum says. 'Meow.' I am not happy about this, I say, sauntering off to sulk. Hang on a minute, there appears to be lots more space on the other climbing frame now. I think I'll go and lay there for a while, until I'm moved. 'I think I'll allow that, as you look so comfortable,' she says, looking over to me but not moving. Hurrah!

Something odd is going on. The Hoomuns are now here all day and every day, saying words that I've never heard before like 'social distancing', 'self-isolating' and 'virus'. Sometimes Hoomum's eyes are all wet and her mouth turns downwards when these words are spoken. When she looks like this, I lay on her and let her stroke me and her mouth starts to turn upwards again.

The stories told on the street about 'The Inside' were that cats have the place to themselves to roam and are able to play as they please, yet I am never alone, and my every move is being watched. There is an upside to this, as they both have what I hear them call a 'laptop' that is perfect for me to sprawl across, although they don't seem to appreciate this as much, as they pick me up each time, muttering something about how can we get any 'work' done with 'this Little Rascal making mischief'.

I don't know for how long I've been living with the Hoomuns, but I'm getting more and more intrigued as to what is behind the dark wall. I've sniffed and rolled across every inch of this giant box, but that wall remains a mystery. Hang on a minute, Hoomum is going through to the other side of the wall, and she hasn't shooed me away!

She watches closely as I enter the large, bright box that is filled with sunshine. I do not rush as who knows what is waiting for me in there. I was right …there IS another cat and she's at least 100 years old! She doesn't move from her spot and looks very comfortable sitting on fluffy pillows. She's seen me and uh oh, she doesn't look very happy.

Hoomum is talking to me now 'Marmalade, this is Wilma. She is very old and doesn't mix well with other cats so play nice please.' I look at her pleading eyes, what a wonderful surprise, I have a playmate! Although she doesn't look as lively as I am, so maybe I'll take it easy. 'Meow Meow,' don't worry I shall make Wilma my friend. Maybe not today, or tomorrow, but I'll try again ... and again ... and again.

I am curled up on the sofa, Wilma walks by, she stops, looks up at me and keeps going. She gets to the other side of the sofa, jumps up, takes one more look at me, then curls herself up. I leave her be.

I am loved, I am happy and I am home.

CONFESSIONS OF A NUN

by Violet Spring

Confession #1, First I must confess I am not a nun

Not in the usual sense of the word. But in some ways I might as well be. I think a lot about my spiritual life, do good works (voluntary work in a primary school and crèche) and haven't had any sensual contact with a man for a very long time...

But I was a real nun once, with robes, in a temple, in Thailand. I'd been having a hot, hot, holiday in Thailand – sun, sea, sand and, OK, a bit of flirtation. I confess the first few days I spent acclimatising. Lying on my bed in my air conditioned room only surfacing for meals. Then I saw what other people were doing – spending most of the time IN the swimming pool, surfacing for a few minutes of scorching sun, then back in again. So I didn't do much sightseeing, but I did go and visit the nearest temple.

The temple complex was beautiful. To me it looked like a modern day Shangri-La. There was a large meditation room with a Buddha statue inside. And outside a couple of huge gleaming golden statues of the Buddha. The complex was flanked by a steep mountain on one side where apparently there were small rooms where some of the monks lived in solitude. In the jungle were cabins where the nuns slept. The monks wore bright saffron coloured robes and the nuns robes of a beautiful lilac colour.

It was hot, but I was glad I'd made the effort. I wandered and wondered around until I met a Swedish tourist. We spoke and she told me she could speak a bit of Thai as her daughter-in-law came from Thailand.

She volunteered the interesting piece of information that, if I liked I could stay in the temple, as a nun. Well, there was a thought! I decided I did like and she introduced me to the nun in charge of admitting would-be nuns, translated for me and arranged for me to stay there. As I was right at the end of my holiday, I couldn't stay long, so I asked if I could stay for a day, but that wasn't enough, she said, it had to be a minimum of two days. So I changed my flight back home and became a nun for the weekend. As you do.

Something for the weekend, Madam? Yes, please, I'll be a nun.

So, why Buddhism? Why stay in a temple? Many years before, I read a book, *The Razor's Edge*, by Somerset Maugham. In it one of the characters, Larry, goes off to study meditation and saw the world from a different viewpoint. I thought it sounded interesting and found myself a meditation evening class. At first I was alarmed by the Buddha statue they had at the front as I knew nothing about Buddhism and it seemed a bit foreign to me. With a question along the lines of 'What's he doing here?' I asked the two tutors. They replied that the statue was symbolic, to inspire people, and they could have used anything, for example, a triangle. I was to find out that turned out not to be the full answer.

In the course I learned two meditations: the Mindfulness of Breathing and the 'Metta Bhavana', loving kindness meditation. They are both very useful to me and have helped my concentration and compassion for other people. I found out you don't have to like people to wish them well.

Oftentimes people say to me 'Oh, I couldn't meditate, I can't make my mind go blank.' But the meditations I learned are practices, ways of bringing you back to your breath, yourself and feeling kind to yourself as well as others. The key is in the word 'practice'. If you don't practice it definitely doesn't work. And good teaching helps. One of the tutors said 'if meditation doesn't help you to be happy, you're just not doing it right.'

At the end of the meditation course, we were offered a three-week course on Buddhism, and by then I was fascinated. The story of the Indian prince who had lived a very sheltered life, but who left the palace to find out the meaning of life and to become himself spiritually enlightened was more inspiring to me than a triangle after all, though I'm sure triangles have their place, I can honestly say I've never meditated with one.

Since those courses, I have been influenced by three great Buddhist teachers.

His Holiness, the Dalai Lama, Thich Nhat Hahn (Thay to his followers) and Lama Yeshe.

His Holiness remains cheerful despite the genocide and devastation wreaked upon his people and country, Tibet, by the Chinese and the lack of support from most of the rest of the world. His message is compassion and showing understanding. 'Kindness is my religion,' he says.

A few years ago I went to a talk he gave in the Wembley Arena. One girl was expecting to see George Michael, but he was playing at Wembley stadium. She freaked when she saw a whole load of Tibetan monks and nuns in their robes. Then there was the ticket tout shouting 'Five pounds for the Dally Lally, five pounds for the Dally Lally,' as if he were selling a bag of bananas on a market stall.

I also saw the Dalai Lama another year as he was walking into the Tibet Foundation. I gave him a tiny posy of pale yellow primulas and white gypsophila I'd prepared, which he accepted. It was shown on Channel 4 News. I was a bit nervous about that as I was living in a small village at the time and attending the local church which was quite conservative and I didn't know what they'd make of it.

Confession #2, Being peace

I learned a lot from Thich Nhat Hahn, a Vietnamese Zen master who has lived in exile for most of his life. His book *Being Peace* is one of my favourite books. He is famous for teaching mindfulness to Westerners. He wrote that suffering is not enough, we must go beyond suffering and strive to be happy. To make peace, you must first be peace.

In a retreat with him, he turned around to me and said 'If you are happy, you can make many people happy.' I confess I do like to make other people happy, and I do want to make a difference. So much so that earlier on in my life, I felt like the weight of the world was on my shoulders. 'Being Peace' really helped me. Get peaceful yourself and do a bit. Don't try and change the World singlehandedly whilst being miserable yourself. That was a relief.

Confession #3, Smiling

Thay also encourages his students to breathe and smile, breathe and smile, breathe and smile... very valuable. I confess I have been told I have a film star smile! I was also told I should smile more. Well I did when I first came to London. I guess it may have worn off a bit, but I'm back to smiling now. I think smiles are great. If we're going to have a counter pandemic, let it be of infectious smiles. It seems like a good time to smile to each other.

Confession #4, Savouring

Then there was the nun I met at Thay's retreat centre, Sister Fong. She was very positive and told us the story of when times were lean and all she had was a boiled egg as a treat, she made it last for a very long time ' Eggs a la Fong' she said. She was all smiles. Savouring is good. I should eat more mindfully but I'm a bit of a gulper. Mum is the complete opposite. When I went out for lunch with her it nearly lasted til tea time

Confession #5, Christmas presence

I love the book written by another great Buddhism Tibetan teacher, Lama Yeshe.

Silent Mind, Holy Mind. It was from a Christmas retreat he'd held for his Western students. He said the best thing you can do over Christmas is not to go 'berserk over presents, Christmas preparations, fighting with relatives etc', but that the best present you can give is to have a peaceful mind. He said Jesus didn't go round giving people presents (though, to be fair, his wine-making skills did come in handy). I bring the book out every year, it's a tonic.

Confession #6, Entering the Temple

The nun in charge of admitting would-be nuns asked me surprisingly few questions about me – in fact, none. Nothing about my motivation, why I wanted to stay or whether I was, in fact, a Buddhist. All she was concerned about was telling me where to buy the lilac robes and small shoulder bag. Robes you wore in the temple, and only in the temple.

I confess, keeping on my robes on properly and decent was one of the hardest things about the stay as they just consisted of material and a rope belt. Some zips and fastenings would have come in very handy. As it was, I confess the robes slipped apart now and then in a most un-nun-like manner.

Confession #7, Nuns on the Run

My holiday at the hotel came to an end, and I started my weekend as a nun. When I got to my room in the temple, with all my bags and souvenirs, I was very happy with it as I'd been given a large room; I had it to myself and it was just by the centre of the complex so I could easily find it. The only let down was it didn't have any beds – just thin mattresses. I later found out that they were purposefully not too comfortable to avoid the nuns and monks having a lie in. Maybe I should try that at home.

After afternoon meditation, a crowd of nuns appeared around me wanting to see my key – which was number one. They then proceeded to usher me to the jungle next to the complex where the small nuns' cabins were.

They didn't speak any English, but led me into one of the cabins. I was not impressed, I wanted my nice, central room, so I kept walking. They came after me though, and showed me another couple of rooms, one to share with another nun. I shook my head and kept walking. They didn't speak a word of English or me of Thai. I didn't like being pursued and I confess, by then, I was nearly at crying point, so I made a break for it and literally ran away with the nuns in hot pursuit. What WERE they up to?

I made my way back to my lovely room. The nuns came shortly after. Then they got it, that I already had a room and that room was number one. But, confusingly there were two number ones and the first room they'd shown me in the jungle was a number one too. Well I was glad we got that one cleared up!

Confession #8, Fern

Shortly after the nuns on the run episode, I met a young Thai nun who attached herself to me in a most delightful manner. I confess I'm not sure what her name was so I called her Fern, as she was lovely and gentle as a Fern. She spoke a few words of English and stuck with me for most of the rest of the weekend.

She was going to stay at the temple for a month and had shaved her head when she first came. It was a few millimetres long when I met her. I had no intention of shaving my head for the weekend and would be hard put to do so however long I stayed. Though I guess there could be a sense of freedom about it.

I confess, when I first met Fern, I thought she was perhaps a little slow as she kept on repeating short phrases. Then I got it, she was trying to keep me mindful, and aware and in the present.

'The Sun, my Heart,' to the Sun.

'The Water, my Heart,' to the fountain.

Confession #9, Meditation blues

Everyone met in the meditation room to meditate. I found it very difficult. Not because of the meditation itself, but because I find sitting cross legged difficult at the best of times and worse with the robes. I fidgeted and fidgeted until eventually a kind soul took pity on me and gave me a chair. The next day a couple of nuns and a monk tried to teach me how to do mindful walking, that didn't go too well either. It's harder than you think.

Confession #10, The rules

I confess I can't remember all the rules even though there were only eight for us nuns. There were the thin mattresses. Then no perfume (as it attracted the opposite gender). No food after noon as it was supposed to be easier to meditate on an empty stomach. The compensation was to get up really early to eat fish stew at six am (full on). Monks and nuns could be single or married as long as inside the temple there were no physical relations. They could be staying in there short term or long term. For different reasons, even to get over a heartbreak, or for some monks, to live in supported isolation.

The monks had way more rules. The ordinary ones had about 100 rules and the ones that were living in isolation had about 250. I never did learn why the massive difference, I don't want to be sexist, but maybe the women just naturally behaved more spiritually than the men?!

Confession #11, Minor transgressions

Of course I didn't do anything really bad, though when Fern took me shopping for a hold-all to take my souvenirs back to England in, she was horrified when I idly picked up a lipstick. Then I must confess I did look lustfully at one of the monks....

Saffron robes and a bare tattooed arm really did it for me. He grinned back. I will never know if he was there for the long term or short term like me.

The other questionable behaviour I did as a nun was riding around in my long lilac robes on the back of a moped with the young lad who had the snack bar. The riding on a moped part wasn't intrinsically bad in itself – I'd seen other nuns and monks riding on mopeds in their brightly coloured robes – but I sensed he had taken a bit of a shine to me and I guess it could be seen as encouraging him, especially as he wanted to drive me off the complex to his family home. Of course I refused and we rode back to the snack bar.

Not sure about the other rules. Yet alone the hundreds of Monks rules. Is that sort of thing on Google?

Confession #12, Carry on smiling

All through my stay, Fern kept reminding me to smile. I thought as a robed nun I should be serious, especially as smiling was taking quite a bit of concentration away from keeping my robes in position, but it seemed that wasn't the case at all. It seemed the 'breathe and smile' routine applied there too.

After evening meditation, Fern and I wondered around the temple complex admiring the large golden Buddhas, lit up in the gentle rain. She looked into the pool.

'The Water, my Heart,' she said, hand pointing to the water then her heart.

Confession #13, Present-able

Another night and the next morning I had to go. I was summoned to see someone who seemed to be senior and I Confess I got the impression he was pleased with me even though I'd made a bit of an unlikely nun. He gave me lots of presents. A whole bundle of the temple's prayer flags, a frieze with a tiger, the symbol of the temple on it, brown cotton wrist blessings for me to wear and give to others and some plastic pendants with a picture of a holy man inside.

Then, the journey homeward, back to England, with my robes but nowhere to wear them, not even Halloween, or in the house, which is a bit of a shame. I have this idea that if I look like a nun, maybe I would feel more like a nun and people will treat me like a nun and I will be a more compassionate, spiritual person. On the other hand, being a short term nun had its advantages. And not being a nun now, I can sleep in my bed and not on a thin mattress. And I can wear lipstick...

SIBLINGS: NOTES FOR A PLAY

by James Thellusson

One

The younger brother is fretting in the playroom. He calls out for help. The older brother steps into the corridor and asks the younger brother why he needs help. What's wrong, he says.

The younger brother is jealous. He could amuse himself and has enough toys to do so but he is worried his mother is with the older brother elsewhere in the flat, alone. He likes to have his brother where he can see him. His mother, too.

But he doesn't say this aloud. Out loud, he replies something's gone wrong with the train set. When the older brother hears this, he starts to run to the playroom because he realises what is about to happen and wants to stop it.

The older brother opens the playroom door. The card table where he laid the train set, painstakingly, is broken. The toy train, station house, station master and several plastic cows are scattered on the floor, stiff feet in the air.

The younger one is sitting on the floor next to the upturned table. Pretending to be injured, he holds his head in his hands. Unconvincingly, he says it was an accident. Ouch. Ow. The older brother starts to cry for the broken train and because he recognizes he can never trust his younger brother again.

Two

The brothers, no longer so young, sleep in separate bedrooms. When they shared a bedroom they did not sleep soundly, were always anxious in the morning. Sometimes, they would stay up all night, not always just because they were arguing.

The mother wishes they would share a room because their new flat is small and she wants one of their bedrooms as a study so she can work from home, have some flexibility. At weekends, it would also be a refuge from them. They treat her space as their own.

One night, the younger brother locks the older brother in his bedroom. He cries fire, fire, fire. The mother panics and rushes from the flat with only the younger brother in her arms.

After five minutes, she returns to unlock her eldest son from his room. By this time, she understands the fire is a deceit. In the same time, the older brother has learnt that if there is a real fire in the future, his mother may make the same choice again and leave him to burn.

The older brother wants his mother to punish the younger brother for his trick, but she is exhausted and cannot face any more drama that evening. She needs quiet to examine the choice she made and what it says about her, if it says anything. The older brother becomes scared of the dark and nightmares. He won't go to sleep unless there is a key in the lock on his side of the bedroom door and a night-light on.

Three

The older brother wonders if his life would be better if he still had a father. He thinks his mother is not up to much when it comes to parenting, especially discipline.

Not that she doesn't try hard. He knows it isn't easy for her to earn a living and care for them because he's been told this by his grandmother, repeatedly. But really he thinks she is just making excuses for her daughter.

Over time, the older brother concludes his friends have better mothers. One of them even has a mother, also a single parent, who takes her son to football and lets him stay up late listening to music. Nothing is fair.

He wonders if life would be easier for her without the younger brother.

He reads James Bond novels and histories of the Second World War. All his school drawings are of battles, matchstick men with revolvers as large as their heads, who should fall over, but don't.

Four

The Parks and Open Spaces team leave a heavy-duty lawn roller, idle, in the communal garden. It's the weekend, so they cut corners to get home early. The older brother has been watching them crush the earth flat.

When they are gone, he inspects the roller. Pulls its iron handle down to the ground or nearly. He feels its springs tense with power. When he lets it go the iron handle swings to the other side, violently. It reminds him of a catapult.

The younger brother is playing at the far end of the garden. The older brother calls out to him. Look what I've found he says and waves urgently. He doesn't say help me because the young brother would sense a trap.

The younger brother runs towards the roller. When he is very close the older brother releases the iron handle which he is holding to the ground or nearly.

There is a sound like elastic snapping. At the moment the iron handle smashes the younger brother's left eye socket, the older brother starts screaming for his mother.

Five

The mother runs towards the two boys and the roller. She has heard the older brother cry out and sees the young brother laying on grass with his hands to his head. From where she starts to run, it is unclear who is hurt or why.

When she arrives, the roller's iron handle is almost still, barely swaying. The youngest is rolling on the lawn. The mother sees blood between his fingers running down the side of his head near his temporal artery. The sound of his crying is like nothing she has heard either of them make before, ever.

The oldest stops crying. He stands by dumb while the younger brother moans and the mother screams. The older brother knows what he has done but he is scared because he also knows he doesn't know what he has done. The mother has forgotten her mobile so begs the gathering chorus to call the ambulance. Please, please, please she begs. Later, questions are asked how any mother could let this come about, but not now, not directly.

The mother takes the younger brother to hospital, leaves the eldest behind with a neighbour. The ambulancemen have to lift the stretcher over the railings because the gate has jammed shut in a conspiracy. The grandmother collects the older brother. She cooks him supper without asking him what happened because she's already heard what happened when her daughter called her from A&E, using a landline in the hospital corridor. She knows talking to him will not help much, anyway.

The older brother goes to his bedroom early. He doesn't want to be up when his mother comes home that night, if she does, because he will have to confess that he is disappointed with her and the choice she made to look after his brother instead of him, again.

Curtain

CIRCUIT

by Oksana Wenger

Chapter One

This was not the Forbidden City. Nor the Temple of Heaven. It should have been. But it was not. And this was not China. Vera was not strolling along that Great Wall, but sitting in her car, here in Trentingham, hesitant, gazing up at the slatted metal gates of Fairfields; gates she thought she'd no longer have to go through.

She sipped some tepid water from her plastic bottle. Was it really only a few weeks ago that she'd felt the sweet shimmer of anticipation, only to be followed by dismay? She'd moved to London nearly two decades ago, but with each passing year her discontentment grew, like the shadow of the birch tree which had only been a sapling when she'd first joined the law firm.

Not long ago Vera had overheard her colleagues describing her as a 'mediocre solicitor' and reddened at the thought. She did have a tendency to see both sides of any legal argument and had become disinterested in boosting the firm's revenue but ended up siding with the various underdogs sitting at the other side of her desk. Most mornings, while striding to the tube station, she wished she were back in Cromgill, on the edge of the Pennines, where the wind soared over mottled greenery; where she could regress into the emollience of her childhood. Her sister, Maria, was lucky enough to still be living there, in their old parental home, and although she had modernised the house, much of it was the same as before – the vegetable garden, the embroidered cushions and Vera's old bedroom.

For the past three years Vera hadn't been to Cromgill as often as she'd have liked. Each time she had visited with Giles it rained and Giles had not packed the right clothing so had caught a cold. After that he'd called Cromgill 'a grey town' and grimaced whenever Vera suggested going there for a 'romantic getaway'. She knew she could go on her own. She did not need Giles's permission, but had somehow never got around to it. Life with Giles had settled into a steady routine. He would be the one to cook the evening meal and at weekends they'd go out for brunch or to a gallery or the theatre. She'd learned to tolerate the dank basement flat with its warped cork bathroom tiles and threatening streaks of black mould. She'd even got used to the unannounced 'little visits' from the landlady. Every now and then however, she wondered what she was doing there.

She finished her water and stared up at the gates. It was only a few weeks ago that she'd passed the Moroccan café, the Polish shop and Indian restaurants of Tooting's cheerful pavements and made eye-contact with the regulars as they pressed their phones to their ears. Buses whooshed through the cappuccino puddles, but on that particular Monday morning, Vera moved nimbly and did not get splattered at all. Just before the weekend had begun she heard some news which lifted her from her spurious treadmill and made her feel cautiously elated. As usual, she'd met Giles in their favourite pub, midway between her office and his, to celebrate the weeks' ending.

'Vera, I've got some great news!' he said as she arrived. He had to raise his voice to be heard above the crowds but seemed more animated than usual. After a peck on the cheek he handed her a cold glass of wine. She smiled at his handsome, beaming face. Had he finally contacted some estate agents? Were they going to move out of that dingy flat, at last?

'We're going to China! You too, hopefully. The conference is in Beijing this year. And partners are invited.'

'Beijing!' Her doubting face glared back at her from the gilded mirror behind him. 'That's a long way to go for the weekend.' She'd accompanied him before to Paris, Dublin and Amsterdam. But he'd said Beijing.

'Not for the weekend Vera, for three weeks! Can you get leave for the last week of July, first two weeks of August?' She did have plenty of leave owing to her but had it not been possible for him to check with her first?

'But, I thought the bank were making cutbacks?'

'Yeah, but we want to get into the Chinese market. It's so lucrative, and what better way than schmoozing with them face-to-face?'

Giles stood outside with her as she smoked on that breezy evening and when her cigarette became a stump they decided to go to a nearby Chinese restaurant. While struggling with chopsticks Giles said they'd be staying in a smart hotel and that much of the trip would entail sightseeing with their Chinese hosts. She'd enjoy that.

As soon as they had finished eating, their waiter began shaking a wicker basket under their noses, ordering them to choose either a fortune cookie or a cigarette lighter. Vera picked out the lighter, the only one in the basket. It was a muted salmon pink colour and on its side, in slanted black print, were the words ' Where there is no…' The rest of the phrase was smudged. Clearly it was not new, but she knew it would come in useful – she was always losing hers. Without showing it to Giles she shoved it in her pocket. Giles had already scrunched up his fortune cookie, mumbling that it was irrelevant.

It was only when her leave was confirmed that Vera allowed herself to feel enthusiastic. She had never been to such an exotic country. Never, in fact, had she been to Asia. On her way to work now, she would browse the Chinese touristic websites and, glistening before her were the bright vermilions of the Forbidden City, the Temple of Heaven and the Great Wall of China. Alluring, mysterious and almost within reach. Her feet now fell more lightly on the office flooring and she no longer felt unsettled when hearing about younger, more bullish people getting promoted above her. Instinctively however, she suppressed from her eyes the gleam of impending temporary escape.

It was the same restaurant that she went to the following week, but this time it was not with Giles but with her old friend Martha. She no longer had much in common with Martha but appreciated her good nature. Martha reminded Vera of a high court judge, the way she listened intently then asked searching questions, compelling Vera to see things from a different viewpoint. She had two young sons and worked part-time, though was vague about what she did. While her head was bent over the menu Vera saw that that her hair had greyed along her parting, like a train track covered in snow.

She had planned to keep quiet about her trip to China but while waiting for the food she blurted it out. 'China!' said Martha. 'How exciting! I expect you're really looking forward to that.'

Martha reacted in the same way as her sister had; both said they were 'really pleased' but Vera couldn't help sensing some latent envy.

'So have you got any plans for the summer?' she asked, trying to nudge the subject away from her trip.

'Well, we're going to Wales at the end of August. But before that I'm taking the boys to Fairfields.'

Fairfields! She hadn't thought about Fairfields for years: That strange place they'd been sent to every summer. For some reason she recalled some raindrops trickling down her neck and shuddered.

'Fairfields! I'm surprised that's still up and running in this day and age.'

'Oh, it's something to do with the boys in the long holidays. I've volunteered there for the past two years.'

'I'm sure you'll have a lovely time,' Vera did her utmost to sound sincere, relieved that she'd be thousands of miles away by then. The waiter from the previous week was nowhere to be seen and this time neither fortune cookies nor lighters were on offer.

The next time she met Giles after work, streaks of light domineered the wispy little clouds and there was a balminess in the air. Tables that had been brought out of hibernation were already occupied by diners. Outside the pubs people were standing around, chatting and laughing, delighting in the start of the weekend.

As Vera got closer she saw Giles looking alone and deep in thought. It wasn't until she was right next to him that he looked up. Without speaking he handed her a solemn glass of wine that had been accompanying his beer on the windowsill. She wiped the rim of the glass with her fingertips, attempting to remove the whiff of staleness and bleach. Giles seemed evasive, not giving a straight answer to any of Vera's questions. He was keen to have an early night. They were going to visit his mum for the weekend so wouldn't be able to have a lie-in.

Giles's mum, Violet, lived in Cheltenham and because they'd got such an early start Vera found the driving straightforward. The front door opened before they'd even pressed the doorbell and there, as if she'd been listening out for them, stood Violet, smiling in her flowery blouse and pearls. Walking with a stick and holding onto the walls, she led them to the kitchen diner. In the middle of the pine table was a vase of tulips, from the garden apparently. They were the same crimson colour as the napkins and Vera exclaimed how stylish everything looked. Violet looked pleased. As they ate she began talking about her neighbours and members of her book club, frequently forgetting people's names. Over the past three years Vera had never heard Violet say anything disparaging about anyone.

'I talk too much,' she said. 'How are you my son? You're very quiet.'

'I'm fine. Just tired.'

'We're going to China. Aren't we Giles? In three weeks' time. On a business trip.'

'Actually Vera…' This was the first time he'd spoken her name for a while and Vera felt as if he were talking to somebody else. She sensed that she needed to prepare herself for bad news.

'Look I'm really sorry Vera, but partners are no longer invited. Because of austerity. We had a big meeting about it yesterday.'

Something shapeless in her stomach plunged towards her feet. For a second she hoped he was joking, but looking at his face she knew he wasn't.

'But… I've already booked my leave…'

'I'm really sorry Vera. I knew you'd be upset.'

Was this Giles's way of telling her, with his mum in the room for protection? Scraping her food to the side of her plate, she mumbled an excuse then stepped out of the patio doors. She needed a cigarette and went to stand under the wooden porch at the side. Perched on the overhanging clematis was a brown bird that began a shrill comforting song. It flew away when Giles approached.

'Look Vera, I knew you'd start going on. It's not actually my fault. We can always go on holiday later on. Keep your leave. You could look for a flat.'

She carried on smoking, unsure of what to say. Not waiting for her response Giles said that his mum had given him loads of chores and that he ought to mow the lawn before it rained. He'd already started walking towards the shed when she heard Violet's footsteps on the gravel. She tossed her empty cigarette packet into the recycling, onto a pile of ready-meal boxes.

'Vera, my dear, you must be so upset.' Violet placed her veined bony fingers on Vera's shoulders. 'Don't be too hard on Giles. He does love you, you know. And so do I. You are a kind, sweet girl, even though you're not really English. Look, I know you and Giles have got a modern relationship but I would love you to be my daughter-in-law.'

Was this meant to be a compliment? Vera chose to accept it as such, too tired to care. In a way she felt gratified by Violet's sincere words, however outdated.

'And I love you too,' she said, putting her arms around her skinny frame.

Giles was the one to drive back to London the next afternoon. Vera found some classical music on the radio and turned up the volume. Twisting her hair around her finger, she stared out of the window, resolving to go and visit her sister the very next weekend.

Maria worked in a care home for the elderly. The old dears, she'd boast, would sing out her name when they'd see her on the corridor, 'like in the old musical', they'd tell her. Because of Maria's shift patterns, Vera had to wait for a fortnight before she could go to Cromgill, shortly before Giles's departure for China. He didn't mind, he said, as he had loads to do before the trip.

She was relieved to be getting away from London, from the office and especially from Giles and his perfunctory attempts at affection. She'd always thought they got on well, mentally and physically, but now she couldn't help looking at him as if she were examining a creature under a microscope and under such scrutiny he looked more like a slug than a butterfly.

When she got to Cromgill, Maria was waiting up for her and so were her daughters Lydia and Luba, bleary-eyed, on the sofa in their pyjamas. Both of them rushed to greet her, giggling, asking her questions and chatting. They all agreed that Vera would come and stay with them during the third week of her leave. But, like Martha, they'd also be going to Fairfields first.

It transpired that Maria had to work on Saturday morning, once she'd taken Lydia and Luba to their drama class. It was deliciously tranquil when they'd all gone and Vera wandered barefoot from room to room, reminiscing about her childhood and, not for the first time, wondering about leaving Giles. The prospect of going to China had drawn them together; she could tell he hadn't appreciated how much it meant to her. She'd often questioned how well they actually got on; but if they split up she'd have to leave the flat and possibly her job; friends were often surmising that it was impossible to live in London on just one salary, even a good salary like hers. Being with Giles was like having a beige security blanket draped over her shoulders and she wasn't sure she was ready to give that up yet.

A fine drizzle loitered at the front door. She put on her hood; she didn't want the rain to make her hair even frizzier. She didn't feel like having a cigarette so walked briskly to the tearoom where they were to meet. Her sister and nieces arrived at the same time as she did and Vera relished being hugged so warmly by them. It was refreshing to hear Lydia and Luba enthuse about the play they'd been rehearsing, speaking in alternate sentences as they devoured a chocolate layer cake.

The girls talked about school while the dirt track they walked on narrowed into a path. Lydia had just completed her first year at secondary school and Luba was due to start there that autumn. The drizzle had now stopped and the sudden appearance of the sun gave a silvery glow to the dry stone walls.

Maria yawned. Vera noticed that her eyes looked a bit bloodshot. 'You look tired. They shouldn't make you do so many night shifts.'

'They're not making me Vera, I want to. It means more dosh. Something you don't have to worry about, leading the life of Riley down in London.' Vera was about to respond but Maria carried on, as if a switch had been pressed. 'Plus, when the old people are asleep, I get a chance to write short stories. My new hobby, I've even entered some competitions.'

By now it had become very warm. Lydia and Luba were some way ahead of them and Vera and Maria copied them by taking off their jackets and tying them around their waists. When Maria quizzed her about her cancelled trip to China, Vera found herself standing up for Giles, especially when Maria whispered that he was a bastard. 'It's not his fault Maria. Anyway I'm not bothered.'

It was late when she got back to Tooting and Giles was already snoring. While she'd been driving she got two texts from him asking about her journey, saying that he missed her, to which she'd replied monosyllabically. Near the kettle she found a handwritten note – Giles wanted to hear all about her visit and that he'd cook something special the next evening.

It was as they were eating this meal that she got a text from Maria asking Vera to call her, urgently. But then, without waiting, Maria called her.

'Vera, sorry if I'm interrupting. You'll never guess what! I've won! You know I entered some short story competitions, well I've won the Mervyn prize! The most prestigious one. I'm absolutely over the moon…'

'Wow, congratulations!' Vera got up from the table and began pacing up and down as she listened to her sister.

'The thing is Vera, I need your help, I'm really desperate.'

Maria's prize, she told her, was to attend a residential writing retreat at the Mervyn Writing Studio, for a whole week. All expenses paid. However, they hadn't given her much notice and this 'opportunity of a lifetime' as she'd called it, was to be in less than a fortnight, right at the start of the girls' summer holidays.

When the phone call ended Vera sat back down at the empty table feeling dazed. Somehow she'd been persuaded to drive Lydia and Luba to Fairfields. Not just to take them there but also to lead the nature walk that Maria was supposed to be doing. This meant that she'd have to stay over at Fairfields. For two whole nights.

BROKEN

by Gill Williams

1

An autumn gust rattled the slates, as rain hammered on the skylight above a modest attic bedroom. A lull, then ear-splitting thunder. At this, the body in the bed escaped the sticky clutches of a nightmare and jolted upright, gasping. A hand fumbled and for a second, the heavy eyes of a young woman were bathed in green as she studied the time. Well that's that then, she thought.

She lifted the flimsy blind and studied a granite panorama stabbed by distant flashes. A blast of hail like canon shot, battered the glass and she flinched. The storm faded but somewhere beyond the glass, among the streets and gardens and messy humanity, a piercing scream. Seconds later another, then a third as the foxes marked out their domain. Alex shuddered and padded back to bed. Across the room, the gleam of silver buttons like a reproach, signalled this day had finally arrived.

2

By dawn it was still tipping down and the thud of rain and hail on the flat roof above the women's locker room drowned out what little conversation there was. But there wasn't much. It was still early and the voices were subdued, as weary women coming off shift, and others arriving, changed into and out of police uniforms and a mix of casual clothes.

'Light shower my arse,' grumbled Laura, as she peeled off every last piece of the running gear pasted like cling film to her body and dumped it in a sodden pile.

A well upholstered blonde buttoned her uniform.

'It's a disgrace,' she said, projecting a voice that was pure estuary, in a challenge to her audience.

Her mates exchanged glances – exasperation mixed with the final dregs of exhausted sympathy. The lack of response provoked a tantrum and she slammed her locker grazing her finger. Seeing her engagement ring, she burst into tears and was immediately wrapped in arms.

'Hey Tina, come on love.'

'It's fucked up and you know it.'

The door opened on Alex, gaunt and weary, seemingly unaware her face was running with water. Silence.

Tears forgotten, Tina headed for Alex stopping inches from her face. Sharpening her spite she waited, dragging out the moment, revelling in the drama. Alex waited too. Go on then, she thought, prepared to accept a gob or a blow without complaint. Tina smiled – game, set and match. She turned on her heel and left, her mates scuttling after. All except Laura, who hesitated.

'Laura! You're late.'

A shrug and she followed, leaving Alex alone in the long grey room. She opened her locker cautiously, braced for something nasty – a payback, but it was just as she'd left it. Not that she would have known if it wasn't. She had no idea what was inside – everything blanked out in the time warp of the last few months. She fished out a carrier; a carton of juice, a desiccated apple and a sandwich – dried to cardboard.

She sat heavily, legs like jelly, longing to weep. The once stoic girl who never cried, had morphed into a raw open wound, where tears were never far away but gave no relief. Oh God, it's time! Her stomach lurched and the trickle of warmth lurking at the back of her tongue, warned her she was that close to throwing up. Christ what a mess.

3

His back to Alex, the Superintendent looked out the window. Now immaculate in uniform and bolt upright, her hair pinned up aiming to look sharp, but also severe – appropriate for the verbal execution she expected, even wanted. But the meeting was devoid of emotion and as the minutes elapsed, she knew the incident would not be referred to, even in the most oblique way – as though it was obscene.

She secured a stray hair, fingers lingering out of habit on the raised birthmark like an ink blot on her neck.

'Give it thought.'

'I have,' she said, followed by a speedy, 'Sir.'

'And?' he was curt.

She shook her head. His mouth tightened as he pushed an envelope towards her, avoiding contact. She opened it and scanned a list of dates.

'Six months?' she asked, struggling to crush the discomfort from her voice.

'Initially.'

She waited for something more, but he was already busy with anything but her. They were done.

'What should I...?'

He flapped his hand – eye contact severed, dismissed.

'Bob. See Bob.'

In the sprawling open plan office, men and women in a mix of civvies and uniform muttered into headsets, stared at PCs, chatted, joked and ate an astonishing variety of food.

As Alex threaded past the desks, the buzz quietened, lips moved, eyebrows raised while everyone affected normality. She knocked at the only private office.

'Yes!' a voice barked.

Bob McNeil, fifties and portly, was surrounded by one hell of a mess of his own making. He waved her in, grabbing folders from a seat.

'Go all right?' he asked and was met with silence. 'Yes? No?'

While she considered, he searched without hope for a home for his papers.

'Speak to me Bradley, I'm not a mind reader.'

'He's…monumentally pissed off. Wants me to transfer.'

He dumped the papers.

'Well yes, I can see that. Quite a few pro's.'

'You can't want me to run away?' Then, 'Like what?' she asked.

'Well...no Tina and the coven to contend with.'

'Seen her already.'

'New bestie?'

'I don't blame her.'

'Well I do and so should you. She's over-playing the grieving fiancé.'

He noticed the envelope.
‘Thought police?’
‘First one today,’ she said miserably.
‘With?’
She read the sheet inside.
‘Porter.’
‘Michael?’
‘Gail.’
‘That’s the daughter then. Don’t know her but her dad’s been around for yonks. Right, make tracks, Stew’s down for a bollocking.’
‘Someone’s at my desk.’
‘That's because it's their desk. You're in B7.’
‘But that’s?’
‘Outer Hebrides, yeah I know.’ His voice softened, ‘Not forever but it is for now.’
He walked her out and noted the reaction.
‘Oy! She's only got one head. Button it,’ he bellowed.
‘Stew! Get your arse in here,’ yelled Bob.
A young PC leapt from his seat.

4

Off a side corridor to nowhere, B7 was an abandoned storeroom crammed with archive boxes. It’s only claim to office status, a metal desk and barely functional chair. Alex turned on the PC. Nothing. She picked up the phone – dead. She looked at the filthy floor and swore. Hiking up her pristine skirt, she crawled under the desk. But they were just unplugged and soon beeping into life.

She blushed when her password was rejected but even the unrestricted part of the system was alien. She needed a login but who could she go to? Running to Bob every five minutes wasn’t on. She leapt up. It was gone twelve. On a day like this the canteen would be rammed. She rushed out hoping to find an empty table. That way if they didn’t want to sit with her, they had a choice.

She joined the queue of strangers – already too late. Where were the people she knew? She watched the tables as she inched towards the hotplates. A table filled. Two left. Then one. Finally her turn.

‘Yes love?’ said the server as the last table was taken.

'Actually I'll...'

The woman was impatient, seeing the large hungry queue behind.

'Fish or?'

'Actually I need to…'

Her voice evaporated. She left the queue and feeling the weight of every eye in the room, replaced her tray and left.

Back in B7, she was furious. Why do that? You're not even hungry. That was true. Food made her retch. She hadn't felt hungry in weeks and only now could manage the occasional ready meal and even that was hard to finish. Everything tasted like cardboard. Her new uniform was a whole dress size smaller and still too loose.

Soaked again after a run to a local shop, she was trying to force down a pasta salad, when a smiling girl bounced through the door and jingled a large envelope in her face. By way of explanation, she held up a card with glittery horseshoes.

'Collection? For Pauline?'

Alex felt a knot in her stomach – was this someone she should know?

'Pauline?' she queried. The girl looked amazed.

'Pauline. You know. Pauline. THE TEMP.' Delivering the last word as though to an idiot.

'Where've you been, Siberia?'

And then the penny dropped and the cheeks blazed scarlet.

'Oh, my God! Born dumb. Sorry, ignore me,' she mumbled and fled.

Alex lobbed the salad in the bin.

Six thirty and she waited. Once was enough. She couldn't face Tina again. Not today.

5

The clinic was a modern cube, incongruous among the row of fifties semis. Alex waited at the door while a tiny camera carried out its examination. A girl in a Chinese-style jacket showed her into the all-white waiting room.

Thankfully it was empty and the girl immersed in a stream of texts, so she took stock of the day, almost relaxed. It was hard to believe – six months ago she'd been a bit of a star, the one to watch, maybe even envied. Everyone knew she was about to be kicked up the ladder and would need to get on with her. Wouldn't have won a popularity contest but she was respected, which was better.

Suddenly right outside, a piercing squeal of tyres and a screech of brakes signalled a late emergency stop. Alex stopped breathing. Hands clamped to the chair.

'Boy racer I bet,' mumbled the girl, oblivious.

After a while, the car started and drove away, Alex took a great shuddering breath, as quietly as she could.

The girl looked up.

'Said it before. That stretch is crying out for sleeping policemen.'

Alex registered a sick discomfort. A buzzer sounded.

'She's ready for you.'

6

By day two she was bored rigid. Bob sidled into the room and plonked himself on her desk.

'Got something for you'.

'Thank God.'

'You're our new rep.'

'Not the? You are joking?'

'Look at me.'

'I am and you're embarrassed. Oh, come on Bob,' she wailed. 'I know less than zero about I.T. Isn't there ---?'

'No. This is it. Get used to it,' he said firmly.

He produced some car keys.

'Shake a leg Bradley, kicks off at ten. Shoreditch.'

She opened her palm and he froze.

'Have you...?' His voice died away.

'Have I what?'

She locked eyes with him.

'Have you driven? Since.'

'Since?' she snapped.

'John.'

She nodded and he surrendered the keys.

'Careful. Slightest thing and they'll be all over you.'

He left, his voice drifting back.

'And if Gerry needs a roll-out liaison, that'll be you too.'

Alex crossed the car park and finding the car, got in and adjusted the seat and mirrors. As she snapped her seat belt on, she looked at the passenger seat, bowed her head and whispered some words.

7

Alex burst into the conference room, checking her watch.

'From Bob?' asked Gerard, a lean man in his fifties with sharp eyes that missed very little.

'Let me guess. Press-ganged last night?'

His eyes narrowed. 'No. This morning!' He laughed.

'Typical Roberto. People, this is Alex,' he announced to the cluster round the drinks trolley and she received a collection of hellos and nods.

'Coffee?' A man by the flask called over.

Alex nodded her thanks as he handed her a cup.

'Alex…?' he asked

'Bradley.' She said very clearly and got the same reaction, just better hidden.

Two hours later, all eyes on the clock.

'Three more cases of RSI,' droned a voice.

'Enough joy for one morning. Desktop roll-out after lunch. I know, I know, stifle your enthusiasm. Back at two.'

There was a stampede and Alex was alone with Gerard.

'Canteen's passable if you don't expect too much,' he said, winking.

'Oh, I've got to buy... '

He stopped her.

'It's all right, I get it. Gets better. But not for a bit.'

After a pause. 'Been there, got the t-shirt,' he smiled.

She wrinkled her brow.

'Before your time. I'm a dinosaur.'

Alex trailed past faceless offices lining an ugly traffic-choked road to kill time. Clumsy with her homemade sandwich, she got a scowl as a piece of tomato landed on the pavement. A vile day – clouds pressing down on the earth, the sky getting darker by the minute and everything grimy, even the stringy flowers in a tub.

Taking a side street to escape the fumes she entered a different world; a cobbled lane, home to a bistro, a salon and a smart boutique which caught her eye. Intercepted at the door by a stern woman, who eyed the food, she deposited the sandwich in a bin and went inside just to be bloody minded. Everything was made for dolls and more than six month's salary, so point made, she left.

A fat drop of rain landed on her face. Then thunder. And seconds later the heavens opened. She looked round. Just up the road, neon bulbs announced SPLINTER, FINE ARTS. She ran to the gallery and bolted inside. After a moment, an androgynous man at a desk looked up and gave her the once over.

'Sorry, I'm a bit wet,' she muttered.

'Stone floor. Drip all you want.'

The rain had set in.

'Take a tour. May as well,' said Marcus.

Beneath a triple height atrium, the curving exhibition space housed a series of abstracts – one of which was entirely black. Alex knew at a glance she didn't like anything.

'No?' he guessed, 'me neither.'

She wandered round, hoping for a cloakroom to dry off. A door beneath the stairs disappointed – an office. Then she looked up. Above the desk a huge photo filled the wall. A child. In black and white – all except the blue toy clutched in the tiny hands and somehow reflected in his eyes.

'How long?' A clipped voice above made her jump.

Marcus pulled her from the room and shut the door.

'Oops. Private.'

Richard Crane, late forties, appeared. A louche, curious looking man who radiated intense, nervous energy. Despite the good hair-cut and expensive edgy clothes, not a picture of health.

'Oh for Christ –'

Marcus cleared his throat, indicating Alex.

Yet again Alex found herself being examined.

'I know you. Do I?'

She shook her head.

'Yes, you're, you're…'

He puzzled.

'Chloe? Is it?'

'Alex.'

'Gavin's sister?'

'Nope.'

'Weird. Well, can I help?'

'No, ignore me. I'm not a real customer.'

'But you're in my gallery.'

'I'm a fraud. I can't afford a thing.'

'Looking's free. But perhaps...you wanted shelter. What do you reckon, Marcus? Would she have come in if it hadn't been raining?' he asked.

'Why not ask her?'

'I might have', she said.

'Only might? I'm insulted. What do you think?' he said waving at the canvasses with pride.

'I think...I'm late for my meeting.' She grinned.

'Coward,' he taunted as she slipped out the door.

He studied her through the glass, frowning, reaching for a memory that would not come.

8

Finally Friday and Alex could breathe again, ready for escape. She headed for the door only to find Tina blocking her way. Suddenly she'd had enough.

'Just say it. Whatever it is.'

Tina grinned.

'My pleasure. You're not wanted here.'

Laura looked up.

'Right, that's it.'

Tina turned, big moment spoilt.

'Who asked you?'

'Not you, clearly. I've got a mouth of my own and I don't need you putting words in it. You can't lay the whole bloody thing at her door.'

'I'll do what I like and you can fuck off.'

'So can you. Think we don't know? Really?'

'What?'

'John was history – about to be dumped. You were shagging Steve.'

Tina gaped and left, red faced. Laura looked round.

'Time someone said it.'

She pointed at Alex.

'She's doing ninety after some slime-bag, and that prat takes his seat belt off 'cause he wants a fag? And that's her fault? Bullshit.'
Some heads nod.
'You've had the week from hell. Fancy a drink?' asked Laura.
'Thanks but there's someone I've got to see.'

9

Rush hour traffic powered homewards along the dual carriageway. Finally a gap and Alex sprinted to the traffic island clasping a bouquet. On the makeshift shrine, rotting flowers jostled with notes and cards, bleached to nothing, pinned round the photo; a grinning man, fag in one hand, pint in the other. She stood before the face.
'I said to wait. You know I did,' she whispered.
Frustration took over.
'But you were always right. Always knew best. Well maybe not.'
She looked at her flowers.
'Waste of good money, wasn't that it? They only die? Fair enough.'
She walked off taking them with her.

10

'Happy Birthday mum.'
Frances Bradley was slumped in her chair, eyes vacant, fixed on the wall. Alex set the flowers on a shelf in the small room.
'Katie?' she whispered.
'Alex. It's Alex.'
She held up a photo of herself.
'See? Your daughter, Alex.'
No response.
'Where's Katie?' Frances whined sadly.
Sandra, a chubby Polish carer bustled in.
'Hello Alex and evening Frances, nearly bedtime.'
'Sorry to come late,' said Alex.
'No worries. We had cake in the lounge. And sang happy birthday, didn't we?' she said, patting the listless hand.
'That's lovely. Guess, I'll be off.'
Her goodbye kiss went unnoticed.

As Alex's footsteps faded, Frances roused agitated, until Sandra opened a battered album and the ritual began. She slowly turned the pages one by one until Frances gripped her hand.

'Katie,' she whispered, 'Katie,' and reached for a photo.

Beneath her fingers a tiny girl with a birthmark on her neck, clutched a blue toy and stared transfixed into the lens.

1CS CRIPPLE STREET

by Astrid Wilson

Chapter One

I can remember the exact moment that life in London struck a new low and I, and Philip too, suddenly thought, this can't go on. I can alsc remember the moment when an abandoned looking cottage in a lane bordered by ancient orchards took hold of our lives. And it was not jus the cottage, it was the family selling it to us, an old Somerset farming family, now in decline. A spell seemed to be cast over us, an irresistible seductive spell consisting of the beauty of the countryside and the richness of a way of life that was receding into the past.

It was 1967 and Philip and I were living in Hampstead. I had jus graduated from the Slade. I thought I was wonderful, an important artis waiting to be discovered. I was painting in the flat but I missed the buzz of the Slade. I missed the company of my fellow students, of visits to the pub, of long conversations over an Indian meal.

Philip was out of a job. He had graduated with a brilliant degree ir Modern Languages and then gone into export. The company he workec for had made some changes and he had been made redundant.

Our flat in Hampstead was quiet. In fact, Hampstead itself was quiet William Empson – do you remember *Seven Types of Ambiguity?* – livec across the road from us. I never did get round to reading it. I was a painter, after all. I painted things – objects and landscapes and people Here is a vase filled with roses, here is a view of distant hills, here is a portrait of my grandmother.

Seven types of ambiguity, yes. It's fine in Hampstead, home of cottor -wool wrapped intellectuals, writers and politicians. But when life becomes real, when the shell cracks, ambiguity melts away. When tragedy strikes it means pain – pain and loss, even death. Death. Nothing ambiguous about that.

We had moved to Hampstead because my sister Tash, short for Natasha, lived there with her husband Hugh. Hugh came from an eminent English family, something to do with the army and there was also a connection to someone dating from the Civil War. He was a barrister. Their beautifully decorated house in Church Row – they even had the original wooden window shutters – oozed culture as well as indicating Hugh's distinguished background. I was very impressed, if not over-awed by all this, because it was so different from our own background.

By contrast, everything about our flat was basic, to say the least. We had just got married. We had gone to Hampstead Registry Office for the ceremony and then had a party at the flat with our friends. Just that. We were desperately short of funds. Philip had signed on and I worked as a waitress in a tea shop. Ends just about met. We paid the rent, stopped having any heating and lived very frugally.

We owed Tash and Hugh a meal – more than one, in fact. Life was very dinner party conscious at that time. Pride had stopped me from revealing to Tash how very hard up we were, pride and perhaps a certain competitiveness. She had made what was known as 'a good marriage'. But then again, I was an artist.

'We've got to invite them to dinner,' I said to Philip one evening.

'There's no got to. There's no money.'

'No, we do owe them a meal – three in fact, counting the pub last Sunday.'

'She's your sister. She should be lending – giving – you money. She's rich enough.'

'It's not like that'.

'Like what?'

'I would never ask her for money.'

'Well. I call that strange, very strange indeed. I thought families were supposed to help each other.'

In the end I prevailed. They were to come on Thursday evening.

I went to Camden Market the day before the dinner. My friends Sally and Peter who were at Chelsea School of Art had created a meal that we congratulated ourselves on as being very creative and even gourmet as well as the essential fact that it was cheap. We were always doing things like that, 'discovering' things which we felt showed how clever and original we were, not at all like the conventional world which we rather looked down on.

This meal consisted of spare ribs served with a stir fry of bean sprouts. I decided to accompany this with sesame seed topped bread from the Greek shop and a salad. This Greek shop – another of our amazing 'discoveries' – also sold a sweetish draught sherry for the ridiculous price of seven shillings, if you brought your own bottle.

'Well,' I said to Philip, 'Hugh must know that artists are poor. It's hardly a revelation.'

'Poverty to him means having to drink Nicolas as opposed to a vintage wine. Do you seriously think he's going to drink sherry, and a sweet sherry at that, with a meal?'

'It's what Sally and Peter drink and Peter's father – oh, look, I'm tired of all this – class, what's done, what's not done. It's all finished, that stuff, it ended with the war. This is the sixties, remember? We've revolutionised everything, all that class stuff. Look at how everyone wears jeans. Everything has changed. We are the people changing things. People like Hugh are stuck in the past. Nobody wants to be like them.'

It was an argument that Philip and I often had. I saw myself as being in the forefront of change. It was not only because I was an artist. It was also because of my refugee background. I felt proud of the fact that we had been in Europe in 1945, almost starving and then in a camp for displaced people. I felt that this was a sort of qualification, although few others seemed to share this view. The perfect storm had taken place in Europe and I been at the heart of it.

When Thursday evening came I began to prepare the meal. Just after seven the doorbell rang. Philip ran to the front door. I followed him. I had decided to adopt a hearty theatrical manner.

'Welcome to the artist's garret,' I said with a dramatic laugh. 'Hardship, poverty – none of that matters. Art for art's sake – '

Hugh began to rub his hands together and I realised that we had only just turned the electric fire on.

'Hardly a garret,' said Hugh, looking around although he must have been aware of the flat's bare contents by now.

'This rather grand room – look at that bay window! – would originally have been the master bedroom. In Victorian times, when those attractive villas were built, around 1870 –'

'I know what Victorian is,' I snapped.

Hugh smiled his ambiguous smile. I never did find out what these enigmatic smiles, quite specifically related to me, meant although I could guess.

'Philip's been made redundant,' I said in a loud, angry voice. 'We're a bit short of cash. I'm afraid it's a rather simple meal.'

Things improved a bit after that. Hugh made an effort to enjoy the meal, which he described as 'highly original'. We then decided to go to the pub and when we were there the evening became a bit more jolly. Hugh insisted on buying us double brandies. 'On me, on me,' he kept on saying, but even that began to grate.

As we walked home Philip said, 'I've had it up to here with London.'

'I have, too.'

'I haven't told you. I applied for a job in the country. Just on the off chance, really. But I've got a second interview and I think they're interested.'

The job was with Clarks, the people who make shoes. He was offered the job and we began to look for a house in Somerset.

Two

It wasn't just Hampstead that had begun to pall. It was the whole art world and in particular my friendship with Julian. My relationship with Julian was platonic. Philip did not believe this and he was very jealous of Julian. However, it was true. Julian was older than myself, only by about twelve years, but when you are nineteen and someone is over thirty they seem to be as old as your parents. In fact, to me Julian was rather like an adopted father or uncle.

By the time this story begins Nicola had left him. I was becoming anxious about Julian and his drinking and I tried to help him. I used to visit him in his house in Camden Town. Artists are very demanding people. They need a lot of looking after. You know – will you do the shopping, cook a meal, wash up, get the paper. I'm busy, I've got to paint.

I met Julian when I was in my first year at the Slade. I had been delirious with happiness when I was first accepted by the Slade. I was always in my room by nine. I worked hard and then I had a break, on my own in the refectory or with other students. Sometimes we went to the pub, sometimes to the Indian restaurant in Warren Street.

It seems strange now, but we talked very little about art. Perhaps it was a form of self-protection. We talked a lot about money, mostly because we were always so hard up. If someone got a cheque for their birthday, it seemed like an amazing gift from heaven. We would instantly blow it on booze or a meal.

William Coldstream was the Professor at the Slade at that time. My own painting style, which was figurative, was virtually a copy of his methodical, academic style. I had a carefully reasoned rationale for painting in this way. I had to defend it, because it was not of course fashionable any more. After all, it was the Sixties. You didn't do representation. Things had moved on. You followed Pop Art or the American Abstractionists.

I have always been religious and I saw Art as a form of worship. Creation was God's work. Creation was beautiful. You painted to try to reproduce the beauty. You painted as a form of worship, to thank God.

Although I was religious I did not like church. Church to me meant people and people meant disapproval. In retrospect, I can see that I was a difficult child. I had a difficult relationship with my mother and I hated school, although in fact I did very well. My mother's friends, and particularly her churchy friends, were very condescending, or so it seemed to me. They said things, like, 'Painting is fine, but it doesn't bring in the bread and butter. You should do a secretarial course, shorthand and typing. Then you will always be able to get a job.' This was exactly what Tash had done and then she had made a 'good marriage'.

I rejected the church and I put painting in its place. I became hooked on the National Gallery which I visited almost every Sunday. I would come out at the end of the day practically drunk with exhilaration. Here was heaven. No judgements here about not doing well at school or who your parents were – just colour and wonderful pictures. This was real life, rich and exciting, the very opposite of sitting with dreary old church people.

Julian came to the Slade during my first term. He was a well known artist. He taught at Chelsea School of Art and he was filling in for a lecturer who was off sick. He was very attractive, with his pale, anguished looking face and dark hair. My friend Sally described him as 'the English Baudelaire' and a lot of the students quickly fell in love with him.

He had a reputation for being very scathing and I was rather dreading his comments on my painting, especially because his own painting style was so different. On the day that he was assessing our work I heard raised voices in the room next to me. Then there was silence and he appeared in my room. He stood there for a bit, looking at the painting stashed against the wall and then at the painting I was working on, geraniums in a pot on the windowsill and a view of rooftops beyond the window.

Then he said

'I don't believe this. I simply don't believe it.'

Despite my resolution not to respond to anything he might say, I felt hurt. I said nothing. In particular, I did not say what I had been mentally practising as a response: 'Coldstream likes what I am doing'. I knew what Julian's response would be: well he would, wouldn't he?

In fact he said exactly that.

'I suppose Bill likes this. It's exactly up his street. Geraniums on a windowsill. Can there be a more hackneyed subject for a painter? In fact, this is not a painting, it's a magazine illustration. An illustration for *Woman's Life* or whatever these magazines are called. To illustrate a story called My Love Won in the End. Or, How I Ended up Watering Pot Plants and Cooking for My True Love.'

I still said nothing, although my feelings fell by another notch. I hoped he would just go away. When he goes away, I thought, I'm going to the student bar. A double whisky, at least. I was feeling down anyway. I had quarrelled with my mother that morning and had shouted that I was leaving home for good, something I really intended to do.

Julian suddenly looked at his watch and said, 'It's one o'clock. Why don't we go for lunch?'

I couldn't refuse. A student refuse a lecturer? An invitation was virtually a command. Oh well, I thought, pie and mash in the refectory. We might even have the luck to meet one of these students who were in love with him. Or perhaps a pint and a sausage at the Wellington. Bill

Coldstream would be there. Then Julian might like to express some of his views on the irrelevance of figurative painting directly to his face.

But to my surprise, he said, 'Let's go to Soho. I feel like proper food.'

I didn't know what to say and I found myself saying yes.

As we walked towards Soho, his manner changed completely. He dropped the sardonic lecturer tone and became a bit more human. He began to ask me questions about my family. I have already told you that I came from a refugee family. My mother, my grandfather, and Tash and I as babies had fled from Estonia as the Soviet tanks approached in 1944. Usually this information was met with a blank look. Nobody had heard of Estonia. Nobody had heard of the Baltic States and of their annexation by Soviet Russia. But Julian knew all about it. He was aware of the situation exactly. What was more, my background, quite often a source of embarrassment, seemed to actually impress him.

'Fly the flag,' he said. 'Don't let it go. This is important. Nationality is important. You are in an interesting minority!'

Another strange thing that happened was that as we approached Soho the atmosphere changed. We left the academic gloom of UCL behind and entered the exotic atmosphere of Charlotte Street. Suddenly there was colour, laughter and people talking in different languages. We passed fruit stalls overflowing with all kinds of fruit and vegetables. There were restaurants from all sorts of nationalities, patisseries with windows piled high with cakes. The smell of coffee and of unusual spices hung in the air. Colour, noise, laughter! How different from the atmosphere of the great hall at UCL with Jeremy Bentham's embalmed corpse sitting there in its box.

Julian took me to an Italian restaurant called Leoni's. It seemed incredibly posh. The outside was painted a dark green. The waiters greeted him enthusiastically but when they looked at me I thought I could sense a familiar feeling of disapproval. There I was, in a tiny yellow mini skirt and a black tee shirt. There was still a bit of paint on my hands. I felt it must be obvious to them that I could never afford to come to a place like this on my own. Did they even perhaps think that I was a prostitute?

The suspicion, will he want to sleep with me, was of course at the back of my mind. Don't drink a lot, I said to myself and have an excuse ready. What could I say if he made a pass at me? We were all incredibly naive at that time and men, especially older men, had a powerful presence. I decided that my line of defence would be to say that my mother was very ill in hospital and I would have to leave because it was possibly my last chance of seeing her alive.

I never did have to use this ridiculous excuse. As we left Leoni's, he said

'I think we can bury our differences? With regard to art? I think we can become friends?'

'Yes,' I said with a shrug. 'OK.'

More Information about CWWL

Our 3-hour kitchen table workshops, limited to a max of 8 students, take place in Chiswick, London W4. We have classes for complete beginners, follow-on workshops, and share-your-work supervised feedback groups.

All kitchen table workshops, at time of publication, have been paused and adapted for online participation.

Our 1-hour online Zoom interactive workshops, limited to a max of 6, are on-going and can be booked via Eventbrite.

Details at:
https://creative-writing-workshops-london.business.site
See also:
https://www.dianechandlerauthor.com/
https://www.blackbird-books.com/
https://intersaga.co.uk
https://theupperroom.org.uk.

Lockdown was eased enough for us to have a socially distanced awards ceremony in August 2020, filmed by Chiswick Buzz TV. You can see interviews with Diane, Stephanie and the winners and hear them reading extracts from their winning entries here:

https://chiswickbuzz.net/blog/awards-for-budding-chiswick-authors

The contact email for frontispiece and rear cover artist is contact@clemilymartin.com.

Blackbird Digital Books
The #authorpower publishing company
Discovering outstanding authors
www.blackbird-books.com
@Blackbird_Bks

Blackbird

Printed in Great Britain
by Amazon